SUPERCHARGED

*THE MODERN-DAY GUIDE TO CREATING
OUTSTANDING LEVELS OF ENERGY,
MOTIVATION AND SELF-CONTROL*

Luke John Harrison
Foreword by Paul Mort

COPYRIGHT

I wanted to die.
Now I show people how to live.

CONTENTS

TABLE OF FIGURES

ACKNOWLEDGEMENTS

I really must say a special thank you to the following people.

Tracy Holmes, my wonderful 'missus.' Your support these past five-plus years has meant a tonne to me. Without you, I wouldn't be in this position, and this book probably wouldn't have been written. I appreciate you every day.

My three best friends, Warwick, Shaun and Nick. Thank you for always being amazing.

My 'Mam' (mother), Maria and Dad, Geoff. Thank you for your ongoing positive impact on my life and your role model influences. Even as an adult, I still listen.

James Holloway, for being an incredibly consistent training partner and friend these past few years, including throughout the pandemic.

Thank you to the entire TST (Total Supercharged Tribe) family for all of their continued support, enthusiasm and belief in what we do.

Paul Mort, my mentor and coach. Thank you for being a positive influence all these years.

To all the guys in Elite X. You're all inspiring men to be around.

Thank you, Matt Elwell, for showing me a different way.

My Tuesday board gaming group that's still going strong. Thank you, Graeme, Tim, Waz, James, Shaun and Nick.

Thank you to David McBarron, a great old friend that always makes me smile.

My staff member and good friend, Adam JP. Thank you for all your ongoing efforts and enthusiastic attitude.

Thank you to all my family and friends who've supported and watched over me over the years. You're deeply appreciated.

Gemma Lynas, thank you for your creative efforts and artwork throughout the book.

The super kind beta readers who gave their honest feedback and valuable time to sit and read early copies of this book. Thank you, Deborah Challice, Lisa Kitching, Lisa Birch, Ali Crooks, Richard Crow, Sam Church, Pete Shaw (Mr Barnsley Barbell), Chris Tibbets and Mark Hallam.

Danny Wilson from Danny Wilson Coaching ('the sleep guy') for helping me with some mega advice and support on sleep efficiency.

All of my ongoing followers, supporters, and even 'haters.' I can do nothing but appreciate you all for being there through the past nine-plus years of my relentless self-development journey.

FOREWORD

BY PAUL MORT

The rest of your life could be your most powerful yet. But, only if you decide, take charge and commit to making sure it happens. The thing is, my friend, you can't finish your year strong without taking charge. Without owning your circumstances. Without owning your behaviour, reactions and decisions. All of it. Are you ready? I know I am.

When Luke asked me to write the foreword for his second book, I was excited as hell about it! To go all-in and show the world, your peers and your family who you really are, what you stand for and what you're truly capable of when you step up. I know this will be a rallying call for you to wake the fuck up.

Over the past 19 years, I've coached people worldwide on how to change their business, mindset, bodies, and relationships to become truly *world-class* in their lives. Luke is one of these men. After winning UK Master Coach of the year twice and investing a serious amount of effort, hard work and energy (and cash) in myself and my business, I came to realise some critical lessons.

Here are some key points that I think you'll find most valuable while reading the rest of Luke's book:

- Information is nothing but facts we try to remember. Transformation comes from *energy*. Therefore knowing what to do and not doing anything is the same as not knowing. In fact, it's worse.
- Questions are the steering wheel of the mind and will quite literally dictate where you go with your feelings, emotions, decisions and ultimately, your life. Your brain is a 'finding machine' and will find what you tell it to find.
- Your energy and what you radiate will either *inspire* or demoralise people.

- The biggest factor in your overall performance and, more importantly, happiness is your ability to manage your state and energy skillfully.

- Not getting a handle on your physical energy (sleep, nutrition, exercise) invites negative energy and emotion.

- Your ability (or inability) to handle other people, and your thoughts about other people, is one of your biggest energy drains.

- As long as you keep blaming other people or things for how you feel and behave, you'll remain powerless.

- The past is nothing more than a present time memory of your perception of a previous event, with your imagination filling in most of the gaps and all of the meaning.

- Read that last one again. It's the difference between handling your shit like a boss and handling it like a bitch. It's the difference between a decision that moves you closer to what you say you want or closer to what you say you *don't* want.

As you very well know, and as the big man with teeth like tombstones and hands like shovels, Mr Tony Robbins, says, "Your decisions shape your destiny."

So, you've decided to pick up this book and supercharge your life? My good friend, Luke Harrison, will show you how to do just that. Give the following pages your time and attention. Make your life no longer a warning but a great example to your family, kids, colleagues, staff, and clients.

Because you're a role model, whether you like it or not. The question is, what kind of a role model are you committed to being?

Let's go.

Paul Mort
2 x UK Master Coach of the year 2020/2021.
Author of Paul Mort Will Save Your Life.
Leader and creator of Unstoppable Alliance.

INTRODUCTION

It's been six years since my last line of cocaine. It's been four years since I was last really drunk and ten whole years since I hit rock bottom and wanted to end it all after the end of a toxic relationship.

My past has been filled with bad decisions. I was burdened with the start-stop-start-stop attitude and relied on food and quick fixes to get me through the day. Suffering from guilt and shame and always believing I was an all-or-nothing person led me to feel sorry for myself and further 'fuck ups' (mistakes) along the way. The triggers that led me to write this second book were the knowledge and lessons I've learned so far in this magnificent journey of self-discovery that we call life. I feel it my duty and obligation to share this knowledge and expertise with you so that you don't have to suffer on your journey to a better quality of living.

I'm a 36-year-old adult male, a former full-time plumber turned personal trainer, and now a full-time fitness and life coach. Currently, I have a thriving coaching business, three cats, a great 'missus' (lady partner/girlfriend), a keen passion for metal music, film soundtracks, retro games, professional wrestling and board games. I live in a small coastal town called South Shields, in the north east of England. With a long history of recreational drug use, weekend alcohol abuse, several failed relationships and frequent bouts of lying and cheating, I was certainly not a stand-up role model. Past behaviours have led me to much anxiety and complete overwhelm.

Since writing my last book, How To Stop Overthinking, six years ago, just a couple of months after my last sniff of the white powder (cocaine), I've changed in many ways. I've changed my outlook, motives, physical and mental strength, and overall physique. Mainly though, it's the mindset (where all our emotions lie) that's changed most drastically. Our mindset holds the power to change our lives from the inside out rather than the outside in. That's why most people are lost, stuck and completely overwhelmed.

I'm not into quick fixes or short-term gains to make lasting change. I haven't been in prison or have a rags-to-riches story. I've never been married or had kids. But I help thousands of people who have. I've never backpacked or travelled the world. I grew up in the small town where I still live. I have a mortgage on a terraced house on a busy road near a cemetery. I still love a Domino's pizza and a good Netflix movie on a Friday night.

But I've dedicated my life, for the past decade, to help others change theirs for the better. I'm here to help you feel more successful in whatever area you feel you need to, or indeed, would love to. Over the years, I've helped thousands of people transform their lives in different ways. I've helped people who need to lose 3-4st (19-25kg) in weight, improve their mental health, so they no longer feel suicidal, or gain self-confidence to leave their miserable jobs or situations and do what they want to do, rather than what they feel they *should* do in their own lives. I've helped people reverse their diabetes and ill health. I've coached people to reignite the passion and physical intimacy in their personal relationships.

Oh, and I, too, am in the most meaningful relationship I've ever had. Since Tracy and I got together over five years ago, we haven't gone longer than ten days without physical sex. That's a pretty long honeymoon period!

Maybe right now, you judge yourself with, "How come everyone else is ahead, and I'm so behind. I'm so useless!" Or you may even fall into the victim trap of thinking, "Woe is me," or "Why does this always happen *to* me?" Use those knockbacks you've experienced so far as setups for comebacks. When comparing yourself to others, rather than feeling envious, ask yourself, "I wonder how they did it? Maybe I could start applying their strategy models?"

Regardless of where you are, I'm here to help you take responsibility and step up. Success leaves clues. I'm here to help you spot the clues and give you the blueprint for your further successes.

WHO THIS BOOK IS FOR

This book is 100% written for you if:

- you keep saying you need motivation
- you're a start-stop person or consider yourself an all-or-nothing kind of person
- you keep making mistakes and end up frequently sabotaging yourself and your results

If, deep down, you desire a less complicated life and are looking for a lasting change of huge impact and highly enthusiastic energy that doesn't leave you the minute you put a book down, this is for you.

However, I must say this. No one's coming to save you. You must empower yourself. If you haven't noticed already, if you're here for a nice, easy talking to, you're probably reading the wrong book. I'm here to kick your arse (British for ass) and tell it to you straight, my friend, to help you genuinely. If you read, study and apply the principles in this book, you can take hold of your own life and supercharge yourself to feeling happier, healthier and stronger. I'll show you exactly how to get started and keep going, no matter what.

You're going to discover how you can get over all the rubbish that life has thrown at you. No matter what you've been through or where you were brought up. Whether you're guilty, shameful and torn down because of your past, or you're anxious, overwhelmed and completely unsure of your future. None of that matters if you're prepared to keep an open mind, an open heart, and you're willing to learn to let go of certain things you know are holding you back. You can do this with the aid of my coaching throughout this book.

If you're simply tired of your bullshit and need a kick up the backside, this book is for you.

You'll discover proven strategies to keep you excited, motivated and energised with a view to a more fulfilling life. Nothing can stand in your way if you're willing to be optimistic about a better future for you, your family and those closest to you. If you're ready to let go of the pessimistic attitude that's likely blocking your progress, and if you're ready to silence the whole "this is crap" or "I'm crap" attitude, I'm here to help you eradicate this.

Armed with the knowledge I've gained over the past ten years of relentless self-improvement and development, I can honestly say I'm a different person now than I was even five years ago. Therefore, this book will be very different from my first book.

After reading and applying my tips, I guarantee you'll also upgrade and transform your life from the inside out. You'll simplify your life by changing for the better and letting go of what keeps you stuck. I'm here to help you create a lasting change.

WHY I WROTE THIS BOOK

I see far too many people falling victim to their own emotions and struggling to get their lives together in my business. Suffering from guilt and shame, they actively destroy their physical and mental health through their own choices. Staying in this 'start-stop-start-stop, I'll do it when I feel like it' mentality leaves them stuck, weak, feeling useless, overwhelmed and disempowered (not a great place to be).

Most people are quite aware of how their own crap ruins their lives. They keep blaming lack of motivation or receiving the wrong advice constantly. They blame the one-size-fits-all approach and people saying, "You 'should' do this or that." In fact, what works for most people is very much a one-size-fits-*one* approach.

These are now my personal mantras in life:

- Make clear the vision.
- Commit to the long game.
- Trust in the process.
- Get excited for the day.

You may be familiar with that nagging voice in your mind that says, "You can't do this." Or perhaps it's, "You've always been crap at (whatever it is)."

And of course, possibly the most destructive thing anyone says and thinks is, "What's the point?" I'm here to give you the tools to help yourself and metaphorically arm yourself daily to wield your sword more efficiently against the battles that play out in your head.

I'm here to help you silence that punishing feeling that keeps you quietly desperate and actively stuck in a rut of bad choices and self-sabotage. I'm here to teach and guide you through a more disciplined and fulfilling way of living, a 'no bullshit' approach to empowering yourself, no matter what. I'm here to help you deeply understand that, unfortunately, growth is painful. It's supposed to be, and sometimes it's filled with dread and anxiety. But that's ok. I'll coach you through how to deal with your emotions as you go on.

I'm not here to tell you it will be easy, but I'm here to remind you it's pretty simple. You don't have to continue to suffer on your own. There are ways to help get yourself into a better state of being and a more energised and in-control state of living. A calmer, more confident, got-my-life-together approach to doing things that will work for you and with you if you're prepared to work for it. But overall, I'm here to get you excited about your life again because an exciting life is a *happier* life.

WHAT THIS BOOK COVERS

CHAPTER 1 - WHERE ARE YOU NOW?

What does supercharged mean to you? This is where I'll take you through a brutally honest self-assessment of your life, with no one else watching, just you (although it may be helpful to imagine me, in spirit, over your shoulder, helping to listen, understand and guide you all the way). Here you're checking in with where you are now in your life. You'll look over several aspects that will allow you to arm yourself with potent data, so you're no longer a victim of the drama in your head, what might or could happen, or what *should* have been. I will delve into how to change your situation no matter how crappy it may seem right now. This first chapter could be the most useful to you.

CHAPTER 2 - THE SEVEN DAILY HABITS

Here I deep dive into the insanely simple seven daily habits that, when applied regularly, can transform your life. I'll share the same habits I use in my coaching programs. From physical health and mental wellbeing to help with sleep patterns, with a sprinkle of science to explain more clearly what you're doing daily, how it affects your brain and your performance in all areas, including the bedroom. I cover the what, why and how of each. Some of this content and professional data may even shock you.

CHAPTER 3 - HOW TO KEEP GOING

You know how to start and get excited about something new. But why is it that the main focus drifts after a few weeks, and the drive you felt at the start dwindles? Then you quickly find yourself demotivated and fed up. You go back so quickly to what's easy. Here I'll help you look into the cycles of motivation and what to do. Not just to get started, but more importantly, the philosophies and actual habits required to keep you going and keep you feeling motivated, no matter what happens around you.

CHAPTER 4 - HOW TO BE COMFORTABLE WITH BEING UNCOMFORTABLE

Things can happen to any of us that are out of our control, and emotionally we can all, at times, crumble. If you think your comfort zone needs to be looked at, here is where I go into that. Here I discuss your comfort zone in detail and how you can manage those times when life hits you hard and makes you feel very uncomfortable. Here you'll delve into what to do when things make you feel super uncomfortable and how to change that fear into a new scenario and thrive on challenges, no matter what life throws your way.

CHAPTER 5 - HOW TO SUPERCHARGE YOUR NATURAL ENERGY

Energy is a key factor in your overall happiness. Here I cover the basics and some more advanced aspects of energy and why it's so key to your performance in life. Here's where I explain why and how to get more of it naturally, without caffeine, stimulants, or anything crazy. In addition, you're going to learn to see your energy as your top priority and ensure that you can stay in a high state of enthusiasm, no matter what.

CHAPTER 6 - SUPERCHARGING YOUR PHYSICAL BODY

Physical health, energy, strength and fitness are my top priorities in life, as they should be in yours. After all, you're no good to anyone without your physical health. I share what I've learned about being in the best shape of my life at 36. I also reveal how I've transformed the health of others, from a 19-year-old college student to a 72-year-old grandma who hadn't exercised in 30 years. They all have similarities in getting in shape and getting healthy. Here I share my experience of nearly ten years as a personal trainer, fitness and health coach, and I demonstrate a path that's not all about what you *should* do. I discuss how to use simple, proven and safe methods to maximise your results, time and time again. This chapter is far from the boring normal you may expect.

CHAPTER 7 - SUPERCHARGING YOUR EMOTIONAL WELLBEING

We all fall victim to emotions at some point in our lives. It's unavoidable. But thankfully, over the years, I've coached with some super heavyweights in the subject of emotional wellbeing. Being able to handle your thoughts and emotions with more self-control and a less negative reaction is a skill that requires development. I'm going to share tactics and stories on how to change your perspective on your emotions. You'll learn to respond from a calmer place with more clarity, a higher perspective and a more useful and positive mindset, no matter where you are currently.

CHAPTER 8 - SUPERCHARGING YOUR RELATIONSHIPS

Relationships are the key to life, whether intimate, personal or professional. I'll go over how to deal with other people's emotions, especially understanding a woman's emotions. Remember, I've written this book from a straight man's perspective, but you can mould the information to your particular situation. Here is where I'll be giving you more insights and tools to work with when navigating the complexity of other humans and how to resolve conflict easier. I dedicate a whole section to sex and intimacy too.

CHAPTER 9 - SUPERCHARGING YOUR WORLD OF WORK

If you're in business, there are things that can help you operate more efficiently. This is down to how you plan, prioritise and purposefully carry out tasks. This helps you find more enjoyment in what you do and make more money while helping more people. If you're in a job, this is most useful for deciding how to progress or even get out of the job you may hate. Maybe you want to start your own business or indeed get into something else that fulfils you? There are plenty of strategies and philosophies on business and professional life that awaits you in this chapter.

RESOURCES

Throughout this book, you'll come across QR codes that direct you to a website with further information, a video or a download link from me on further coaching or something of value which I'm sure you'll enjoy. It'll also put a voice and face to these words as I'm personally presenting all the bonus material, which I think is always great for you, the reader.

Occasionally I quote from studies and resources that I've researched to support what I'm saying. These are annotated with numbered references detailed in the Endnotes section at the back of the book.

If you're unfamiliar with a QR code, it just looks like loads of little squares jumbled together on a page. You just take out your smartphone, load up your camera as if you were about to take a photo, and simply scan your phone over the square below. The phone will bring up a web link for you to access straight away where you can meet me personally. How brilliant is modern technology? Try it now. Open the camera on your phone and scan the screen over the image below and meet me for real.

KEEP IN TOUCH

If you want to contact me, more detailed contact information is at the back of this book in the Keep in Touch section, including my personal email, social handles and other ways to stay in touch with me, along with some information on my other programs you may like to get involved with in the future.

Let's get into it!

PROLOGUE

It was New Year's Eve in 2011. I went to the local pub for a few drinks with my then-girlfriend, several friends and their family members. As the night went on, we both had a few drinks. I was drunk but not 'wasted' (overly drunk). I was having a good time and laughing with my mates (friends). That was until my girlfriend started to act irrationally and became an embarrassment to be with as she was wasted on alcohol.

We started arguing in the pub, so we went outside for some air. She started throwing a 'hissy fit' (temper tantrum), smashing her bag against the wall as we raised our voices at each other. I remember sitting on a bench while she was pushing me again and again. I grabbed her by the chin and said firmly, "Stop pushing me."

At this point, a couple of guys could see things were getting out of hand. I was triggered and told them to "fuck off and stay out of it." I was angry. She was furious. I knew she'd had too much to drink, so I called her mam (mother) and told her I was putting her in a taxi home. She wasn't happy with being pushed into a taxi. I told her, "You're too pissed (drunk). Go home and sleep it off."

The taxi left, and I thought I could relax with my friends and their family. However, she asked the taxi driver to turn around and return to the pub. We couldn't get another taxi. I was reluctant to leave her, so I told her we'd have to walk home, about one and a half miles away, at one in the morning on New Year's Day. We set off in pitch black. She was still mad about the taxi incident and decided to start jumping on me, clawing at my face, pulling my hair and trying to kick and punch me. I pushed her to the ground hard. I apologised and picked her up.

"Listen, this must stop now!" She could barely stand on her heels. She became increasingly violent, jumping on my back, so I pushed her off and then picked her back up again. She tried to run away into the fields screaming, and I dragged her back. She fell and bruised her knees. She launched herself at my face again, and of course, she fell again. Shoes wrecked, I pulled her to her feet. Then her coat ripped. The walk home seemed to take forever. Her elbows exposed, she fell again.

This carried on all the way home. Now, I'm a big strong guy, so I wasn't physically hurt. I was able to push her away, restrain her, and keep her at arm's length. However, as we got home, she was in one hell of a state. She had bruises and cuts from the numerous falls, with dirty clothes ripped in parts. Looking down at herself, she got even angrier. I decided to go straight to bed.

She followed me. We started arguing again in bed. "Whatever. Aye. Fuck off. Shut up!" We screamed at each other, taken over by alcohol-fuelled arguing. I remember the final moments of her grabbing my face and saying she should get something from downstairs and stab me. At this point, I lost it. I grabbed my girlfriend by the shoulders and threw her off the bed. Her back hit the radiator, and I open-handed slapped her as hard as possible. You could have heard a pin drop at that moment. Absolute silence. It was the only time I'd ever raised my hand to anyone, let alone a woman. I immediately apologised. She was shocked. So was I.

What had I done? "This must stop now," I said. Thankfully, it did. Shortly after, we crashed out asleep. The following day I woke up a little heavy-headed but deeply furious at everything that had happened the previous night. When she woke up, I told her what had happened in detail. She remembered nothing. It was a complete blur to her. It was as if her body had been possessed, and it certainly seemed that way. Once the afternoon came, I drove her home and told her our relationship was over.

That evening, I got a phone call from her parents. "Luke, we've seen the state our daughter has come home in, with bruises and clothes ruined. We've taken several pictures, and we're taking them to the police. It looks like she's been assaulted." I could appreciate how it looked, but that wasn't the case. I was devastated. I admitted straight away that I'd slapped her hard because of her behaviour. But I never punched her or kicked her. However, it certainly looked that way.

Over the next few days, I went back to the pub to see if they had CCTV of our incident outside. Unfortunately, they didn't have it turned on. I tried to speak to a couple of the guys there. They said they were too drunk to remember it clearly. I knew she'd been very aggressive outside at the start of the whole incident. I even had my mam call my girlfriend's mam to convince her I wasn't a violent person and vouch for my personality. I couldn't bear the thought of someone believing a false story about me. People will almost always believe what they see or hear and not what is factually accurate.

After this, my mind swam with negative, low and destructive emotions. I was struggling *big time*. My ex-girlfriend and I kept our distance from each other after that night, but I kept hearing stories of people saying things like, "Hey, did you hear Luke beat up his girlfriend on New Year's Day?" It was deeply embarrassing and humiliating, and I felt alone as I lived on my own at the time in my first house.

Even though I had people around me in my life, some fantastic friends and family who were very supportive and know I'm not a violent person, I still felt alone. Admittedly, I could be angry at times. But I was never physically violent to others. I drove aimlessly all over the local area during this testing period because it kept me sane.

For months, I tried to prove I was in the right. It was exhausting. Mentally exhausting. Several people wouldn't believe me. Being overly concerned with what others thought quickly destroyed my self-confidence and ability to feel happy. I was sinking and drowning in overwhelming emotions that I didn't know how to deal with, such as guilt, shame, anger, frustration, regret, and confusion. It became too much, and I hit rock bottom.

During one of my routine long drives, I drove to Durham, about 25 miles from where I live. As I walked around one of the indoor shopping centres, I passed a pharmacy. I went to where the pills were displayed and scrolled my eyes left and right to see which ones I could buy to "end this shit right now."

A few seconds passed. At that moment, I wanted to die. I felt dead inside, weak, pathetic and vulnerable. I felt as if everyone hated me. To be fair, I hated myself and what I'd become. A 'pisshead' (drunk) with a big ego and several 'bad women habits.' An angry 'dickhead' who frequently dabbled in cocaine. A short time before that evening, I'd been unfaithful to my then-girlfriend. She found out by reading my phone, which sparked the incident on New Year's Day.

I was selfish on several occasions where I would 'session' (get drunk and take drugs) most weekends and generally not be the most stand up of role models. In my 20s, I didn't know who or what I was.

After looking at some pills at this pharmacy, a voice in my head said, "Get out, Luke." Something made me walk away. I walked outside the pharmacy, leaned against the glass, and mentally talked myself out of it. "Luke, you can't go on like this. You have to sort yourself out."

The rebuilding started. Shortly after this, I left my plumbing job, which I despised. I started my self-development journey and my own personal and group training business. I started reading books, attending courses and investing time and money into mentors and coaches. I tried to be a sponge and soak up what I could from people further ahead than me.

My drinking habits reduced dramatically. I started looking after my body in the gym and taking care of what I put into it. But more so, I started taking care of what I watched and read. I stopped watching the news altogether. I stopped watching full porn too. It's astonishing what this did for my mental health and my ability to be positive.

The drug-taking didn't stop immediately, but I drastically reduced the intake. It took another five years till I finally ended that behaviour. I'm straight up sharing the truth about this time in my life as it was my lowest point. As a result, I learned several life lessons that you can take into your own life. I've narrowed them down to the most powerful four:

1. **It's far more useful to be at peace with what you've done and where you've been than it is to prove yourself right.**

Back then, my ego was inflated, and I needed others to believe my side of things. But I was exhausted trying to explain myself. Perhaps you, too, have had a similar situation where someone thought something about you that's not true, and it's crippled you. But you can't change their mind. It's *your* mind that needs to change to move on.

2. **Understand that you always play an equal role in the whole scenario.**

When you stop playing the victim, blaming others for being aggressive, a 'bitch,' not good enough, etc., and start seeing the truth, things will shift.

The truth was that I chose to get back with my girlfriend several times before this incident. I played an equal role in everything. I had to accept responsibility for my flaws and my mistakes. I lied and cheated, I was angry and could be a 'dick' at times. Everything changes when you start to accept responsibility for your past, rather than pointing the finger at others. You'll notice that every time you point your finger, there are three pointing right back at you.

3. **You always get what your standards allow.**

I should have left the first or second time my girlfriend and I split up. Instead, we got back together six or seven times. We were like insecure school kids who couldn't be apart, rather than responsible adults who hold their standards high and realise "it's just not working." You get what you tolerate in this life. With higher standards now, I'd no longer accept this behaviour from anyone, not even myself.

4. **When you're not following a great system or routine, your mental and physical health will suffer enormously.**

Your health will deteriorate if you're living for the weekends, not held accountable to anyone or anything, or you're just coasting through life like I was. For the rest of your journey in this book, I'm going to share with you everything that will lead to you living your happiest, healthiest and strongest life yet, but through a more valuable and structured routine.

CHAPTER 1

WHERE ARE YOU NOW?

Questions steer your life's direction and mindset. When I was a plumber and deeply unhappy in my job and general life, someone asked me, "Could you see yourself living this life, the way you are, for the next 40 years, day in and day out?" That question made me completely rethink where I was in my life.

The problem with most people is that they don't like to answer uncomfortable questions. Honesty, these days, is a dying habit. They get used to lying to themselves and others, saying things like, "I'm fine," or, "I'll be ok," when they may be struggling deep down. I also understand most people don't want to feel like a burden to others, telling people their problems in detail and where they think they need help.

THE UNCOMFORTABLE QUESTION

I will ask you an uncomfortable question to help set you free and find out truly where you are now.

I ask you to rate your life right now out of ten. Give yourself an honest assessment of your overall life. Score one as low, rock bottom, depressed, exhausted, lost, lonely, and lacking direction. Score ten as being on cloud nine, the fittest, happiest, healthiest and most vibrant you've felt in years, feeling 15 years younger than you are and buzzing with confidence.

What number would you honestly say you're at on an average day?

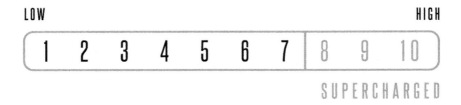

Figure 1: 1-10 Supercharged Scale

I understand this can be hard to answer. I ask this question to everyone who comes to work with me before we get started. It helps cement a reality check on everything and points you towards where you say you want to go. But to answer this more effectively, you're going to go further than just overall life.

I ask you to break this down into the key areas of your life. You're about to do an honest assessment of each of the following areas:

- personal energy
- physical body
- emotional and mental health
- relationship
- world of work or study

You may find that you're very fit and active and, therefore, a seven on the physical scale. But you're lonely, have no sex life and generally are miserable outside the gym. You'd score three or less on those scales. You could have an exceptionally supportive partner who loves you dearly no matter what, always compliments you and has your back constantly. Therefore you'd rate your relationship at an eight or nine. But you're deeply miserable in your mundane day job and would score a two or three.

You may be 'minted' (wealthy) with loads of savings, very sensible with your money, have a great income, a big house, expensive car, clothes and great holidays. But you're overweight, hate the way you look and hardly ever get laid. Therefore you score a nine for money and job, but just a two or three for body, energy and relationship.

Here's your first task. Grab a pencil and score yourself out of ten in your key areas on the following few pages.

TASK: YOUR PERSONAL SCORE

1. PERSONAL ENERGY

This is your overall day-to-day energy and enthusiasm (not your fitness, I'll come to that). How much drive and natural energy do you have that doesn't rely on energy drinks or stimulants? Do you find yourself slumping at 11 AM or 3 PM? Are you constantly 'knackered' (tired) and maybe have six coffees and three energy drinks a day just to keep going? Assess yourself honestly on a regular day. What is your day-to-day energy, optimism and enthusiasm for your life?

Figure 2: 1-10 Personal Energy Scale

2. PHYSICAL

How fit, active, strong, healthy and in shape do you rate yourself in your physical capacity? Perhaps you can sprint up the stairs and run around on your feet all day with no problems. Are you active daily? Do you achieve ten thousand minimum steps? Maybe you hate your body shape, and it's causing you confidence issues. Do you like yourself in your clothes?

How would you rate your strength levels regarding what you can do with your body? Could you do ten pushups? Could you perform 20 sit-ups?

Figure 3: 1-10 Physical Scale

3. MENTAL

How good is your mental health out of ten? How would you describe your emotional resilience? Do you crumble at any form of negative judgement? Do you judge yourself harshly and hide away from new opportunities? Do you take things to heart too quickly? Would you say you're emotionally stable when you get a knock back? Score yourself honestly out of ten while taking into consideration these questions.

Figure 4: 1-10 Mental Scale

4. RELATIONSHIPS

Let's break this one down into two areas: physical intimacy and other relationships or friendships. Consider the following questions. How is your sex life? Is it frequent, passionate, deep and experimental? Do you regularly have a date night with your partner?

How is your relationship with your parents? How would you rate your relationship with your kids? Do you feel like the best role model for your kids right now? How have your friendships been recently? Have you seen and made time for your friends in the past few months? Consider all these areas of relationships and score as honestly as possible. You'll know which particular area needs to be looked at most. I'll come to more individual strategies for improvements later in the book.

a) Physical intimacy

Figure 5: 1-10 Relationships (Physical Intimacy) Scale

b) Friendships

Figure 6: 1-10 Relationships (Friendships) Scale

5. WORLD OF WORK

How fulfilled are you in your position at work? Do you feel valued as an employee? Do you think your business allows you plenty of freedom and time off? Would you say your job role or business is fulfilling for everyone involved? Do you genuinely *love* what you do? Are your hours reasonable and flexible enough to accommodate what you'd love to do with your life? Do you feel you earn enough money and are rewarded for your efforts? Consider all these questions, depending on your situation, and score accordingly.

Figure 7: 1-10 World Of Work Scale

Now that you've given yourself an honest assessment, you'll discover where you need to make improvements immediately. You'll notice that some bits are working, and some aren't, but hey, there's no judgement here. You shouldn't judge your early efforts, as that's just self-abuse. Even if your scores are low and you may feel bad about yourself in some ways, that's ok. You're discovering now that some things aren't working. Therefore you're becoming more self-aware, and that you need to change your approach. Most people will bury their heads in the sand (ostrich syndrome) using work or something else to pretend nothing is wrong. Most won't ever audit these parts of their lives with true honesty.

Just think about that for a second. Most people will never look at their life with an honest self-assessment for fear of damaging their ego. So pat yourself on the back, my friend, for getting this far and being so honest. You've made a start, and I'm genuinely happy and excited for you. Armed with this knowledge, you can now decide where you need to be more consistent with your focused efforts. The information you're about to digest in the coming pages will help you stop procrastinating and get you moving *fast* on getting your act together.

Looking at the above self-assessment of your personal energy through to the world of work, you can see you've marked six scales in total. Therefore, your overall score will be out of 60. You can also now see where in your life you're lacking and what areas you need to improve the most. To get your overall score, add up all your scores above.

For example, if you scored a six on all six scales, your overall score will be 36 (six multiplied by six scales). If you scored four on three scales and seven on the remaining three scales, your overall score would be 33 (four multiplied by three scales plus seven multiplied by three scales).

Circle your overall score below.

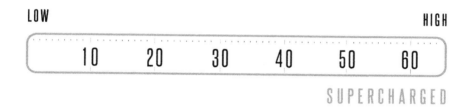

Figure 8: Overall Supercharged Score

WHAT'S IN YOUR GAP?

Your gap is 60 minus your overall score. You may have noticed in Figure 8 that you need to score at least an eight in all areas of your life to be supercharged. That's what this whole book is about and what it will help you achieve.

Let's say you score three on physical body, which is the most common answer I get when I ask people about their body and fitness. Within that gap of three to ten, what could be in there for you is "a 3st (19kg) weight loss that I've held onto for decades." Or it could be "doing the physical challenge this year I've been meaning to do for years" (perhaps a run or competition of sorts). Or maybe it's something like "a toned body so that I feel confident enough to take my shirt off in the summer." Or it may even be "just to be active every day without pain in my knees and back."

Of course, it's going to be very individual. But I want you to consider before you get into the strategy, what is it specifically inside your own gap? Be as clear as possible. Another way to phrase this would be, if we met 12 months after you'd read this book and had time to implement the strategies, what would you need to see, feel and experience to rate your particular area an eight, nine or ten out of ten?

There is no point in analysing someone else's wants or even placing yourself in a position of saying what you should want. What do you *really* want? No bullshit, just straight-up honesty. What is missing that you know would make you fulfilled and happy if you had it right now? This important question releases you from any guesswork about where you're really at in your life.

For example, if you scored a seven for your world of work, you're clearly happy in your job or business. Maybe all you desire here is some minor adjustments and upgrades to feel better about your situation. Perhaps you wish you had one extra day off to spend with the family? But, let's say if you scored two for your energy, you feel it's super low, and you're tired and lethargic all the time, you need to pay far more attention to that score. You need to consider making significant changes moving forward. Your list of what you desire here would be a lot longer.

There are no wrong or stupid answers. They are what you want and desire. I always say, "Want what you want and don't feel any guilt for it." From here on out, don't sweat anything. I've got your back.

> **Want what you want and don't feel any guilt for it.**

Before I get into the how-to, I need to raise something that I feel is important, having been a victim of this in the past. Most humans are very stubborn. They're set in their ways. They hate to be wrong, and anything that questions their deeply held beliefs is a load of crap, stupid or daft. They often feel, "What's the point in that?" This perspective is one I've witnessed from many people I've been around and is one I used to hold onto in the past.

Your mindset becomes very closed if you stop learning after school or higher education. "You learn something new every day" is usually just a nice phrase people use when they hear something they've never heard before. It seldom leads you to fully learn something new as a useful habit or valuable skill. The main reason is that, for most people, their minds are closed off and naturally negative. They can be pessimistic and often in denial, even if the evidence is staring them in the face.

You know this to be true. For example, when someone is so fat they're heading for diabetes or a heart attack, they make it ok to smoke, drink and overeat. They tell themselves "until it happens," correct? Or when their partner asks them to stop being lazy and give them more attention, they continue to go to the pub or watch TV for hours. Only when their partner decides to leave for good does it become a bigger problem.

You know what you *should* be doing less and *shouldn't* be doing more. But to change your ways, you must be more understanding. To a certain extent, we all have a fixed mindset. But to change your life, you must be open and willing to new ways of thinking. Ways that may even trigger, upset, or anger you at first might be the most useful way to start thinking.

Most people only hear what they want to hear, not what they *need* to hear. It's easy to be pessimistic, just as your parents probably are (I hear this a lot). Your colleagues probably complain a lot, and the people on your social feed are always moaning. Is it any wonder it's so hard to be positive when you're constantly around people like that? It's hard, but it's not impossible. It all starts with having a more open mind to new perspectives. I'll introduce you to new ways of thinking.

NEW PERSPECTIVES

A NEW PERSPECTIVE ON YOUR PERSONAL DAY-TO-DAY ENERGY

What gives you energy? Yes, carbs and caffeine certainly do temporarily. But real, authentic energy comes from within. You need water, sleep, movement and adequate hydration to stay healthy and energised. But one thing I'll say about energy is that it needs to be of the utmost importance in your life. In other words, a priority.

There is nothing more important than you feeling good. Please remember that. Without energy, you simply cannot feel good. Most people have low energy levels because of how they treat their bodies and minds. Examples of mistreatment are late nights, junk food, too much alcohol, too little rest, and too much screen time. Not only that, their overall attitude drains their energy. Attitude is everything. A little more optimism and enthusiasm will go a long way towards keeping your energy levels high and keeping you motivated.

I'd like you to consider your claim that you lack motivation. It's not motivation you lack. It's energy. Energy is life. Your energy should be one of your top priorities, and you should protect it at all costs. Just as you would protect your kids or animals from all threats, you should guard the entrance to your energy field from anyone or any*thing* trying to take it away from you.

When people are 'knackered,' they're no good to anyone. The tired dad shouts at the kids and eats and drinks things to fill him temporarily. Yet these things leave him feeling even more empty and tired. The exhausted mother slips into a feeding frenzy of wine and ice cream to fill the void created by the lack of energy because self-care isn't a priority.

We all choose the easy stuff when our energy is low. We all make worse decisions when we're tired. But with a highly energised life, everything is more manageable. Do you want my best advice on your mindset regarding energy? Make it your number one priority every day. I'll talk about strategy in the next section.

A NEW PERSPECTIVE ON YOUR PHYSICAL BODY

A vehicle on the road and moving every day needs to be looked after well. But even a Ferrari polished to a mirror shine is useless without an up-to-spec engine that performs. Your body is a vehicle that needs to take you right to the end of your journey (life). Your body is meant to perform. It's not meant to always look like a Ferrari. Yes, you can wear a suit, slap on some makeup, do your hair nicely, or put on the best filter on your phone to make you look ten years younger. But if the inside is full of rubbish and it doesn't run well, it's going to slow you and ultimately let you down.

Your vehicle needs regular maintenance. Here comes an eye-rolling cliche. "You wouldn't put petrol in a diesel engine." You know that's true. It's the same for your body. Pizza, chips, ice cream, chocolate, and alcohol are all lovely things that are ok in moderation. But they're not designed to be ingested in large quantities or too frequently. Your body needs fuel for performance, not just food for ease and taste. It needs highly nutritious fruits and vegetables, a mixture of fats including nuts, seeds, oils and, of course, good levels of protein from fresh fish and meats to fuel it to move. If you're plant-based, your body would require highly nutritious protein alternatives.

Consider what your philosophy is on your own body. Have a good think about this because it's time you treat it with more respect. You only get one body. You can't trade it in or resell it, but you can upgrade it by treating it well. I recommend doing so by understanding these two principles.

1. MOVEMENT IS MEDICINE

With fear being physical (felt inside the body), the more physically capable you become when training your body for strength and fitness, the more you increase your capacity to handle pressure. The more you move, the more efficient you become and the more courageous and confident. You will begin to release negative emotions through the vent of physical exertion as it gives you a positive outlet for many of the frustrations you may carry.

During our morning training ritual, I always say to my Total Supercharged Tribe (TST) members, "This is not just an exercise session. It's a training opportunity. Fucking treat it that way!" The only two reasons you should ever miss your physical training is illness or injury. You should never miss training because:

- you're a little tired
- you're not feeling motivated
- you've got a lot going on
- you're nervous
- you're depressed
- you're anxious
- things need to settle down first
- you've got a big day ahead
- you're on holiday
- it's Christmas, your birthday, an anniversary, etc.

You must treat your exercise or movement as a ritual or prayer. If you were religious, you wouldn't miss a day without praying, right? Prioritise your training, along with what you choose to fuel and hydrate your body. That is, the fuel it needs, not the food you desire at that moment.

2. HEALTH IS WEALTH

This is a philosophy that I keep reminding myself and my clients, especially those who work long hours and are always busy. I know there can be much pressure to perform in a job or business, and the more money there is for the taking, you often can't refuse it. But if your health is suffering while your bank balance is rising, you can't fully enjoy that money. I'm also confident your family would rather have you in the best state of health and energy, rather than rich, fat and angry.

The question is, will you ever regret getting healthier, more energised, fitter, stronger and more confident right now before it's too late? Also, what many people don't realise is that the fitter and more healthy you become, the more money you can make from work because of the energy and confidence you build. If you don't prioritise your health, eventually, it will have to take priority, whether you like it or not.

A NEW PERSPECTIVE ON MENTAL HEALTH

It's worth repeating here that *nothing* is more important than you feeling good. For many years, the anxiety I created inside my mind was challenging. Most of us know someone who's been affected by suicide or mental health problems in some capacity. Perhaps you may be in a place where mental health is a daily struggle. The following few paragraphs could be vitally important in helping you change your view on your mental health.

If you haven't realised already, your physical health, movement, and what you put into your body directly impact your mental health. The 'movement is medicine' philosophy has helped me and many people I know get out of their heads and into their bodies, which is very influential for positively impacting mental health.

Consider if you would describe the following aspects as 'crap' currently:

- your life
- your appearance
- your sleep
- your body
- your mental health
- your anxiety
- your depression

Consider this. When it comes to your mental health, do you say "*my* anxiety" or "*my* depression?" When you believe something is yours, you refer to it as 'my.' It becomes your property, and you don't want to let go of it. You may not realise this, but *your* anxiety, body, and life become part of your identity and part of the person you truly believe you are. To drop or change the person you think you are would mean you might not know yourself. Creating uncertainty about identity is something you always unconsciously try to avoid. So I'd further urge you to consider that having a big problem gives you something certain, even if that problem is perceived as 'crap' or 'rubbish.' It keeps you safe and with a level of certainty.

Imagine if you didn't have anxiety. You might not know what to do. Imagine if your body was in great shape. You might be scared you'd lose it, and people may judge you and say, "I knew you couldn't keep that up." Or others may say, "You've changed!" They don't want to hang around you anymore. Being in a place where you're sure of where you are will keep you able to handle it. What I'm saying here may be very new to you or an entirely new perspective on what you perceive to be awful in your life.

I understand how our mental health makes us judge ourselves harshly. I get it. In reality, it's hard to be positive. Finding things to complain about and see as negative is easier and often gets someone significance and sympathy from others because they can relate. Through relating, they don't feel alone, and they don't feel too exposed. It's often easier to keep their issues because they're accepted and invited into certain circles because of them.

You'll begin to see this as true when you start going to the gym and stop getting drunk every weekend. You'll realise how much those people you used to hang around with loved and wanted you to keep your previous problems. When you start doing well, most people can't relate. Sometimes you'll experience rejection. Consider whether holding on too tightly to what's 'bad' in your life and what you feel is your 'problem' actually keeps you feeling certain and therefore stuck in your ways.

An alternative could be to consider whether it's time to let go of those tightly held beliefs about what's *yours*. Start focusing on the solutions to getting rid of those issues and upgrade your identity to become someone you've always wanted to be.

A NEW PERSPECTIVE ON RELATIONSHIPS

The purpose of a relationship isn't to make you happy. The purpose of a relationship is to help you live your highest self. This philosophy has saved me a tonne of heartache. Many of us think that other people should make us happy. At times they do. But other times, why do they push our buttons so hard that we want to strangle them to death (don't deny it).

The reason relationships end is because most people perceive too much negativity, challenge and conflict without the opposite feelings of positive support and agreement. They see too many drawbacks and downsides and feel the relationship no longer serves them, so one or both have to let go. Most get into relationships for the wrong reasons, mainly to see what they can *get* from the relationship. Everything changes when you enter a relationship based upon what you can *give*.

However, it's safe to say that those you love the most often trigger you the most, and that's the balance of the universe in action (without getting too spiritual).

- You can't have a negative without a positive.
- You can't have support without challenge.
- You can't have ease without hardship.
- You can't have acceptance without rejection.
- You can't have an agreement without conflict.

Deep down, you already know this to be true. When something is going right, something *will* go wrong at some point. When things go wrong in a relationship, things go right somewhere else in another relationship or part of life. The problem is that most people are too quick to adopt their natural, pessimistic "this is crap" attitude, the "why does this always happen to me" victim mentality, so they only see the downsides. This is normal, by the way.

There are equal amounts of ups and downs in everyone's lives. Most people just fail to recognise them. In terms of relationships, I think a great simple way to deal with everyone who plays a role in your life is to understand that every single person will provide a mixture of ups and downs, support and challenges, love and fear, and positivity and negativity. And yes, the ones you're closest to will likely give you more of those things. Remember, everyone is always doing what they believe is best for them. It's often hard to navigate relationships because many people don't understand why they have conflict and challenges so frequently from those who supposedly love them and who they love. But that's the meaning of balance. You can't have one without the other.

A NEW PERSPECTIVE ON WORK-LIFE

Whether you're in a job or own a business, speaking from a man's perspective here, your purpose or mission in life is often linked to your professional status. To be in the position of a leader, bringing in money, providing for loved ones, and being free to be 'on purpose' is masculine energy at its core.

Women, of course, also thrive in a professional arena. No doubt there's a considerable percentage of very professional, successful women. It's awesome to see the world evolving this way. But in my experience and thorough observation, it's mainly men who take their professional work-life to be their prime purpose and mission, even over their family. Regardless of whether you agree with that observation, we all spend so much time in a professional capacity that work-life needs to be exciting and fulfilling.

Money is an energy that always congregates and flows towards the highest perceived value. When it comes to money, you get paid based on the value you bring to the marketplace, whether self-employed or in a job. The higher up you go in a company, the more value you bring to that company. Likewise, if you're not being paid handsomely in your business, you're not giving enough value to people. Maybe you do provide value, but not enough for the number of people you need to reach.

If you want to make more money and be more fulfilled in your role or position, here's a shortlist of things you can do to make yourself more valuable:

- Be more personable (have higher standards than the crowd and be prepared to go the extra mile).
- Remember people's first names.
- Make others feel good when you're around them.
- Arrive on time.
- Have enthusiastic and curious energy about you.
- Learn skills that make people's lives more convenient.
- Care for others' results.
- Give people an experience.
- Have a firm handshake.
- Look people in the eye.
- Be kind and compassionate, but firm where needed.
- Sell people what they want, then give them what they need.
- Save and invest 10% of your earnings at the end of each month (pay yourself first).

WHY WE REALLY DO WHAT WE DO

Unfortunately, many people fall into the trap of living their lives how they believe they should, rather than how they want to. For me, this meant getting into a secure job as a plumber several years ago, with good pay, flexible working hours, paid holidays, sick pay and pension benefits. Getting a mortgage, an Audi car and getting drunk at weekends was normal life for me ten years ago. Until I realised I was pretty miserable. I hated my job. I was living the life and doing the things I thought I should.

Leaving in 2012 for an utterly unsecured position of self-employment and a new healthier lifestyle was frightening. However, although it was damn scary and uncertain, I saw enough benefits to changing my life and enough drawbacks to staying stuck that it was worth it.

I'd like you to understand that you've likely followed a path of pleasing others or having a 'should do' attitude. Maybe your parents pushed you into what they thought you *should* do, and you've found yourself miserable and unfulfilled. Remember, you'll always do what you value highest and what you see enough benefit from, even if the behaviour is stressful or potentially harmful. No matter what, you'll always find time, energy and money for what you value highest, even if this means doing what you say you hate.

When you perceive enough benefit from a particular behaviour and enough drawbacks from not doing it, you'll always adopt that behaviour. For example, you may smoke. You know it makes your breath stink. You probably know you shouldn't do it. You understand and realise that it might give you cancer. But you also know you'd go crazy without it. It's your number one way of staying in control. You'd feel left out of the conversations with other smokers. You'd miss out on the entitled time away from work. You'd miss the relaxation it provides you. You'd not know what to do with your hands if you didn't smoke. You feel like you'd lose a part of yourself if it weren't there, as you've always been a smoker since you were young. Deep down, you feel you might lose your identity, and people may reject you if you quit.

Therefore, quitting seems too hard. You're already getting so many positives from the behaviour, so why stop? With enough perceived benefit *for* you (the positive value), you'll always find time, energy and money to support and carry on that behaviour. You'll carry on without requiring any willpower or motivation. You'll keep smoking because there's too much drawback in *not* doing it, and you perceive too much benefit in carrying on smoking.

That is until the drawbacks of this behaviour outweigh the benefits. Let's say you catch your son smoking at the age of 16, and you're mortified. Your uncle gets diagnosed with lung cancer two weeks later after 30 years of smoking. You're close, and he tells you to your face, "Please stop smoking while you still can." You get rejected by a pretty girl you've been attracted to for ages because she's disgusted by your smell of smoke. You run up the stairs in a hurry, only to find yourself gasping like someone 30 years older after three seconds of exercise. You start to notice how yellow your fingers are. Then you look down at your younger son playing with his toys and think, "Is this what I want him to grow up like?" After stacking those drawbacks or negatives, you decide enough is enough, and you quit the behaviour.

This area of human behaviour is fascinating. You'll always continue a particular behaviour that gives you enough perceived benefit. You'll continue even if the behaviour is bad for you. You'll do things that might even kill you because you see enough perceived benefit and get something from that behaviour. And yes, it's the same for drinking, binge eating, killing yourself in a job you don't like, avoiding social environments and much more.

The opposite is true too. You'll always avoid behaviours in which you perceive enough negatives, even if that behaviour is good, such as not smoking. Even though you may say you don't like a particular behaviour, you'll continue if you perceive enough benefits from continuing that behaviour.

You're always doing what you believe has the most benefit for you. Your current position will stay the same until you consciously perceive enough drawbacks to your behaviours and enough benefits in adopting new behaviours. Only then will you have one of those "this has to change" moments. This is why most people end up staying where they say they don't want to be. Isn't that interesting?

SUMMARY

Remember, clarity equals power. This phrase, when understood fully, will help you through a lot of challenging emotions. Now that you've honestly assessed where you are, it's ok if your life isn't where you want it to be. It's all fixable. It's not broken. No one is broken. This is a personal perspective, but I believe no one is broken. They've just found ways to be very inefficient. They've discovered several ways not to set themselves up to win. But no one is broken.

In reality, you don't need to fix yourself. You need to upgrade yourself. By feeling upgraded, you'll notice personal progress more, which will lead you to higher levels of useful transformation and further happiness. The time for being too harsh on yourself is done. You now know where you are in your life after your honest self-assessment. Now you need to think deeper about where you're going.

So, based upon what you've learned so far in this book, let's create a quick action plan to get you kickstarted.

TASK: ACTION PLAN

In the area of personal energy:

The one quick action I believe I can take this week to help improve this area of my life is

---

In the area of physical body:

The one quick action I believe I can take this week to help improve this area of my life is

---

In the area of mental:

The one quick action I believe I can take this week to help improve this area of my life is

_____

In the area of intimate relationships:

The one quick action I believe I can take this week to help improve this area of my life is

_____

In the area of friendships and relationships:

The one quick action I believe I can take this week to help improve this area of my life is

_____

In the area of my world of work:

The one quick action I believe I can take this week to help improve this area of my life is

_____

Remember, there's nothing more important than you feeling good. Your philosophy really matters. How you see things and what they mean make a whole world of difference. Although this may not be super clear right now, it'll all fall into place for you as you read on. I'm excited for you now. Chapter 5 onwards will delve specifically into how to upgrade your weak spots. This is where I talk about strategy. However, I'd strongly suggest not skipping out on Chapters 2, 3 and 4 as they reveal a deeper understanding of how to succeed daily. They also show why you don't stay motivated and how to keep going with momentum, no matter what happens.

CHAPTER 2

THE SEVEN DAILY HABITS

The seven daily habits you're about to be introduced to have a specific focus on raising your energy to supercharged levels. With more energy, you can more easily prioritise your efforts and feel multiple benefits ripple throughout your life. If you want to change your life, you must adopt healthier, more useful daily habits. After all, you're a direct product of what you continually *do*.

Over time, you develop a set of daily habits that you do, consciously and unconsciously, which ultimately make up your identity (who you believe you are). You get up when your alarm goes off. You drink coffee. You watch the news, you shower and brush your teeth. You drive to work, type and click buttons, and eat lunch. You scroll through social media, watch TV at night, carry out specific duties, etc.

Something to bear in mind is that you don't need motivation or willpower to engage in your unconscious habits. I'm talking about typical, average habits you unconsciously carry out without really thinking about them. They're usually things you've done for years and do on autopilot.

I've heard many people say, "It's 70% diet, isn't it?" I can understand why, as you can't 'out-train' a bad diet. Figure 9 on the next page represents a healthy and balanced lifestyle. Of course, as soon as you start eating well, coupled with great exercise, you'll notice your results accelerate.

If you were to measure a healthy lifestyle using Figure 9, you'd see that if you only trained and exercised but still ate badly and had a lousy sleep routine, you'd achieve just 33% of optimal results. If you added in an exceptional

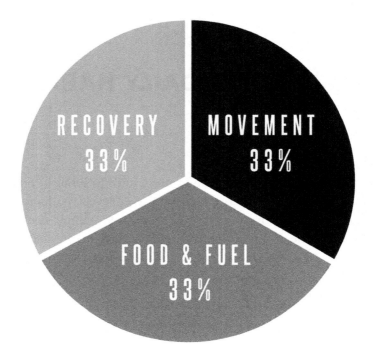

Figure 9: Pie Chart Of Healthy Balance

recovery and rest routine, you'd get 66%. But, if you combined the seven daily habits and looked after yourself in a balanced way that included movement, recovery and great food choices, you would technically be near 99% (literally, supercharged results).

If you're wondering about the remaining 1%, it's a kind reminder that nothing will ever be entirely flawless, perfect or complete. Your journey of a balanced healthy lifestyle is only truly 'finished' when you're dead and gone.

All these habits are essential. Getting a good, consistent balance of them together gives you the most life-changing results. With the seven daily habits I'm about to share, you may find you do one or more of them unconsciously or consciously already. The great thing about having these seven habits is that it makes it easier to track your results.

Using my simple checklist, you can work out how many of the seven habits you've achieved. View it by scanning the camera on your smartphone over the QR code image below.

The past ten years of helping people get into shape physically and mentally every day have shown me the importance of these seven simple daily habits. When prioritised and executed consistently, they are by far the most impactful ways to completely rebuild your lifestyle, leading to a happier and healthier version of you. The science is there, and I've done a tonne of studying, so you don't have to. I'll go into further detail as you progress through this book, but the main thing to note is that I've seen firsthand the results these habits have given others. Results not only for myself but for my clients and people I've helped to upgrade and transform over the years.

At first, these actions will have to be consciously adopted i.e., they may require some willpower and effort. But when something is repeated often enough, it becomes a habit, and that's when less motivation is needed. Now, let's look at the seven habits, from 'performed' earlier in the day to later. Then I'll break them down individually.

THE DAILY HABITS TIMETABLE
MORNING (AM) HABITS:

1. Write down *one* thing that will get you excited about the day ahead.

2. Elevated heart rate/sweated for at least 15 minutes.

DAYTIME HABITS:

3. Two to four litres of bottled water drunk (depending on body weight).

4. One big salad or a large portion of green vegetables (added to one meal).

EVENING (PM) HABITS:

5. No food two to three hours before sleep (ideally go to bed on an empty stomach).

6. No phone or screens 30-60 minutes before sleep.

7. Get to bed one hour earlier (minimum seven to nine hours sleep).

Where do these habits fit into the Pie Chart of Healthy Balance (Figure 9)?

- Habit 2 comes under Movement.
- Habits 1, 3, and 4 are under Food and Fuel.
- Habits 5, 6, and 7 come under Recovery.

These habits are pretty straightforward, not too complex, and you may think, "These are all pretty simple." But, the question is, how many are you doing every single day? As you may well imagine, some of these wouldn't be super easy to just do on autopilot from the onset. However, I'm going to explain to you why these are so important and just how potent they can be when executed regularly in your own life. In greater detail, let's look at why you should be doing these seven daily habits as regularly as you can.

HOW TO CREATE THE SEVEN DAILY HABITS

HABIT 1 – WRITE DOWN ONE THING TO BE EXCITED ABOUT

Of course, you could think of something to be excited about and feel excited about it for a moment. But how often do your thoughts get clouded by worry, overwhelm and other negative emotions? Putting pen to paper or stating out loud, preferably amongst others (my clients and I do this in our online Supercharged Accountability Group), makes things *real*. It cements your intention for the day. Let's be honest here, how easy is it to get caught up in the "I'm having a crap day" or "rubbish week" mentality?

Do you have nothing to look forward to, except for maybe the weekend when you can get 'pissed' and watch more TV? I know at first this is hard. You genuinely have to think hard about what you could be excited about in your life. But it doesn't have to be extravagant. In our online group, the members state daily exciting things such as preparing a nice dinner, enjoying the warm weather, taking the dog out for a long walk after work, finishing a long-overdue project, taking the car for its MOT, or watching the football. I've pulled these genuine examples from our group this morning as I write. It could be just as straightforward for you too. Just find something.

The reason why is simple. Your brain is a 'finding machine.' In the morning, you're immediately preprogramming your brain to have something to look forward to when it's susceptible to inputs. Something that hasn't happened yet and doesn't give you anxiety. Imagine if you had something to look forward to every day, even if it was small. Something that makes you excited. Imagine for a second how much happier you'd feel day-to-day if you had that.

Guess what? You can do it because you create excitement from within you. The more you exercise this 'excitement muscle,' the more consistently you feel excited and the more of a habit you'll build for creating a more thrilling life. You create your good feelings. You prime your morning by focusing on what you choose. Why not give yourself something to look forward to daily?

It's really magnificent, the power of this simple daily exercise, but you can't just *think* about it. You must write it and make it real. Try to let go of your pessimism and trust in the process. It's even more powerful when you share it with others. Could you share it on your Facebook? Every morning, I've got loads of people sharing their daily excitements within my accountability group, and we all bounce off each other's energy. It's really amazing!

What do you *get* to be excited about today, my friend?

HABIT 2 - SWEATED / ELEVATED HEART RATE FOR AT LEAST 15 MINUTES

Simply put, your body is designed to move. It's not intended to sit around all day. When you move your body, you create feel-good hormones. When you exercise, you get that burn, and you feel that high afterwards. Many runners know this as 'runner's high.' It's caused by endorphins, which are feel-good chemicals created as your body's response to pain. The pain of exercise makes you feel fantastic!

You must move to feel good. Not only is it bad for your joints and heart health to not exercise regularly, but it'll also negatively impact your mental health. You'll feel more depressed, low, tempted to eat rubbish food, and hide away from the world. I always say that at least 15 minutes of activity for your physical and mental health each day will keep you in tiptop shape. It won't only boost your energy but change your mental state, making you feel more relaxed, calm, energised and focused. Who wouldn't want that?

It's entirely up to you what exercise you do. It could be a brisk walk, sprints, a run, rock climbing, weightlifting, CrossFit, boot camp, swimming, football, tennis, jujitsu, boxing, yoga, dance, or just walking the dog. One isn't necessarily better than the other if you're not consistently doing one in the first place. What matters most is that you enjoy it and get something out of it.

It annoys me when people argue about which type of exercise is best, whether for fat loss, weight loss, mental health, etc. The best exercise is the one you consistently do, you enjoy doing it, and you can keep it up. It's really that simple.

> *The best exercise is the one you consistently do, you enjoy doing it, and you can keep it up. It's really that simple.*

My TST members and I do a mixture of bodyweight conditioning, weights, kettlebells, yoga, boxing, body combat and different styles of team training. We move the body in ways that are challenging and fun. Some come to our private gym in South Shields, and others join in with us online, usually via Zoom or Facebook Live, wherever they are in the world, for a great morning routine. We do 40-50 minutes of live hard training four days a week. We do 15-20 minutes of lighter training like yoga or easier challenges on the other days.

You may say you hate exercise, but I believe you just haven't found the one that stimulates you. You might love running, so run. You may detest running, so try weight training. The process is hard, and you're going to feel a little useless at first. But you'll never regret the activities you try.

You can't avoid the following facts. If you're a 25-year-old and recover quickly, you've got your choice of anything from heavy boxing, CrossFit or strength training. Whereas if you're 55, you feel your body doesn't recover as well as it did 30 years ago, you might want to start swimming, bodyweight training from home, or even brisk walking as it has less impact on your body. However, lifting weights is something I believe you can start at any age.

I can't make this point any more simple. The point is to be active daily, for at least 15 minutes. Raise your heart rate, breathe a little deeper, sweat and feel the muscles work so that your heart, body and mind are all challenged.

Adopt a little more self-care and compassion into your daily routine. As you keep doing this habit, you'll realise that when you treat yourself right, you'll treat others better too.

HABIT 3 – CONSUME TWO TO FOUR LITRES OF BOTTLED WATER (DEPENDING ON BODY WEIGHT)

Answer this honestly. Are you drinking enough water? Unfortunately, most people aren't, so most people lack hydration levels. Most people forget the benefits of having good hydration levels, such as superior cell health. In case you're not aware, your overall health depends on the health of your cells. After all, trillions of them working together make up who you are.

You'll have less brain fog with higher levels of hydration. You'll crave less unhealthy food when you're drinking more water, and your athletic performance will improve in any kind of activity. Here's an interesting fact. "Distance runners slow their pace by 2% for each 1% of body weight lost through dehydration. Sweat loss of more than 10% body weight is life-threatening," according to the research[1] conducted by Nancy Clark, Board Certified Specialist in Sports Dietetics.

Your life literally depends on you drinking enough water. You're probably aware you can live up to three or four weeks without food, but only three or four days at the most without water. So why not tap water? It's an interesting and highly debated subject, but research[2] shows that tap water contains many chemicals. These chemicals meet legal standards and aren't supposed to threaten your health. They have, however, been shown in some studies to cause many problems over time, ranging from increased risk of cancer to neurological, immune and gastrointestinal damage. Sure, you could drink tap water for 40 years and not have any issues, but then find it's contributed to cancer or early-onset dementia by the time you're 60.

It's up to you to make your mind up here as there's evidence to support both sides of this argument. I choose bottled water every day. Yes, there's a risk of plastic contamination if the water has been lying inside the bottle for a while.

However, it's preferable to the risk of contaminated tap water. I always prefer to buy water in glass bottles. In my opinion, the water tastes better from glass, and I have the opportunity to recycle.

With this thinking (I always like to think long term), my honest suggestion for daily drinking water is to pick one of these two solutions.

1. **Get a five-stage reverse osmosis filtration system fitted under your kitchen sink.**

   It's not too much work for a plumber or someone competent to fit these systems. They help remove many harmful contaminants from tap water, such as fluoride, chlorine, lead and nitrates. It works by pushing the water under pressure through several increasingly smaller filters and finally through a semipermeable membrane, essentially trapping all contaminants. It's about £200 for the kit and then £50 a year for filter changing. In my opinion, tap water also tastes better after this small process. I swear by it.

2. **Consider an alkaline water system that runs off your tap, such as a Kangen water filter system.**

   This is a more expensive option. I'll be investing in one soon to get pH 9.0, highly alkaline drinking water. The more alkaline your internal body is, due to what you put into it and generally how you choose to live, the healthier you are.

No matter what you choose here, what matters most is you're hydrated enough daily. If you don't drink enough water, you must start. Your life literally depends on it. You'll be surprised at how much mentally clearer you feel and how much more energy you have day-to-day as a result.

HOW MUCH WATER DO YOU NEED?

This depends on your body weight. A heavier person has more body mass to hydrate and therefore requires more water. According to the late Dr Batmanghelidj, in his medical research[3] before his passing in Nov 2004, "You should never go more than 15-20 minutes without sipping water. If you're thirsty, it means your cells are already dehydrated, and you should look to consume half your body weight in ounces daily."

To make this easy for you, let me demonstrate a simple calculation I did to work out how much water I needed daily:

1. 33oz is one litre of water.

2. My bodyweight is 81kg, so that's 179lb (rounded up).

3. Half of this is 89oz.

4. 89oz divided by 33oz equals 2.7 litres of water that I require daily.

Let's say you weigh 90kg (around 200lb). If you did the same calculations, you'd require 100oz of water daily. That's the equivalent of three litres of water each day.

As you can see, the heavier you are, the more water you'd require. The lighter you are, the less you need. Most people will likely need two to four litres of water, depending on their body weight. This should be spaced throughout 24 hours daily.

HOW TO PHYSICALLY DRINK MORE WATER

I've had this complaint more times than I care to remember. People say, "I'm never off the toilet when I drink more water." I usually stare blank-faced and respond, "Yes, that's what happens, you moron, you piss more because you're drinking more. Stop complaining!"

Joking aside, to see it differently, consider that you're flushing out toxins and hydrating your cells, giving you better internal health and mental clarity. Going for a few extra toilet trips is a minor inconvenience compared to the major health benefits of drinking more water.

Now I've gotten that out of the way, here are five ways to make drinking your water more achievable:

1. **Drink a pint of water upon waking.**

    Before hitting the coffee, grab a glass and slam dunk one whole pint down your neck. I like to add a teaspoon's edge of bicarbonate of soda to add a little flavour and act as an extra gut alkaliser. You could use a squeeze of lemon instead as lemon also has an alkalising effect when inside the body.

Adopting this habit as a ritual each morning will kickstart the rehydration. You've been dehydrating overnight while you sleep, and your cells will need that good old H_2O upon waking. Yes, it's not easy at first and will require some force and even willpower at the start. But the more you do it, the easier it gets and the more of a habit it becomes.

2. **Purchase a one to two litres capacity, ugly (or unbelievably mesmerising) and unavoidable water bottle.**

If it's not visible, you'll forget. A large, visible water bottle will be a constant reminder for you to drink if you keep it within arm's length and let it take up physical space on your desk or in your immediate vicinity. Make it unavoidable. I've bought a one-litre capacity copper bottle that's shiny, large and has my Supercharged Wristband wrapped around it to remind me of the energising benefits of the water.

Make it visible all day, every day. Those little clear, see-through bottles or the water cooler tower that's on the other side of the office is no good if it's not constantly within arms reach. Here's a rule to remember. Treat your water bottle with the same distancing rules as your phone. I bet it's never out of arm's reach, right?

3. **Turn it into a challenge.**

Who doesn't love a challenge? Who doesn't love completing a challenge? Buy a clear water bottle and put markings on the bottle at specific points. This will be a way to measure consumption at certain times throughout the day. So, for example, by 11 AM, you'll be at the third line down. By 3 PM, you'll be six lines down, etc. Have a visible target for the day and get someone else on board. Why not make it a competition amongst your work colleagues?

4. **Add some flavour.**

   Water is often boring to drink for many people, so they won't drink it, which I've always found a little crazy. Make it easy for you to want to drink it. Buy some frozen fruit and add it to your daily water bottle to infuse the water with flavour throughout the day. Or how about squeezing a slice of fresh lemon or lime? This is good for an extra alkalising effect as well as adding taste.

5. **Follow these rules for when you're out and about.**

   You should always have access to a drink, no matter what. Carrying a heavy, bulky and ugly two-litre water bottle around with you is highly inconvenient. It can be difficult to remember to drink water if you're out and about all day and don't have your bottle handy. Make it a priority to buy a small disposable bottle of water from your local shop every time you're out and just keep it in your pocket.

   If you're going to the pub, regardless of whether you're drinking alcohol or not, try a fresh lime or blackcurrant and soda water. This can be either a refreshing drink between pints or a hydrating alternative to alcohol if you're driving.

HABIT 4 – EAT ONE BIG-ASS SALAD OR A LARGE PORTION OF GREEN VEGETABLES WITH ONE MEAL

Technically, from an Englishman's perspective, this should be 'big-arse' salad. But saying that out loud sounds like a big bowl of hairy butt cheeks, which doesn't sound appealing! So, for visualisation, 'big-ass' is what I'm going to call it.

Most people these days simply don't eat enough vegetables. The majority of people I speak to rarely have even one portion of vegetables daily, let alone a mixture to hit their five-a-day target (you'll remember hearing about five-a-day in school). And no, potato salad with baby potatoes slathered in cream or mayonnaise with a few tiny sprinkles of green herbs does not count as one of your five-a-day. Only morons would think that's a salad. Neither does a side salad next to your main course consisting of 3 tiny spinach leaves.

Here's the deal. Without vegetables, you're going to struggle to get healthy. I know vegetables can be boring. It's why I've dedicated the following pages to help make them as sexy and appealing as possible and remind you why they're such a vital part of your everyday habits. If you don't eat your veggies, you're more likely to overconsume other high-calorie foods. Not only that, you may find it difficult to feel full or satisfied because you'll lack the fibre found in vegetables. This means you'll overindulge and eat a higher quantity of other high-calorie foods to feel satisfied.

Remember, more calories equals more weight gain. Plus, vegetables are powerhouses of nutrition containing high quantities of vitamins and minerals. If you don't eat vegetables, you could become deficient in specific nutrients and become more sick, lethargic and tired as a result. Not to mention, the longer you go without being optimally healthy by consuming a good, varied balance of nutrition through your food intake, the more likely you are to die or have a serious illness.

There, I said it. It's a bit morbid, but you need to listen. You need to have your five-a-day as if your life depends on it. Consider this question to put things into perspective on how influential vegetables are in making you eat less crap. When was the last time you ate three bananas in a row? Probably never! Because one large banana, or two small bananas at a push, has enough fibre and nutrition to give your brain and belly the feeling of satiety or temporary satisfaction.

When was the last time you ate a big bag of Doritos crisps, a Kit Kat Chunky, a bag of M&M's, or drank two to three cans of fizzy drinks? Did you then shovel in a packet of fruit pastels and eat a pizza within a 20 or 30-minute window? If you could eat a thousand plus calories of rubbish food in one sitting, why would you struggle with just over a hundred calories of banana?

Think about this. The majority of the crap food most people eat is riddled with sugar and chemicals to get them to consume more and then buy more. I'm not even mentioning what it does to their brain and gut health, along with leaving them craving that future hit of salt, sugar, fat and chemicals.

Your body never craves food. It craves calories and nutrition. After a reasonably sized portion of salad, with mixed leaves and other vegetables, your body will be a hell of a lot less likely to gorge on crap. It'll also be intoxicated with vibrant vitamins and minerals that will help your immune system and the overall function of your cells and organs. You feel more tired when your diet sucks. When you become healthier, your energy increases, as does your brain function.

However, be wary of salad dressings as they can often contain a tonne of hidden calories and chemicals. If you're watching your weight, even a healthy-looking salad could have 500-700 extra calories because of the dressings used on it or offered in a packet for you to add as flavour.

THREE WAYS TO MAKE YOUR SALAD MORE APPEALING

Check out my big-ass salad video below.

To combat the mundane boredom of a simple salad, or to fight off the extra calories contained in most dressings, here are a few options to help:

- Make the salad yourself, so you know what's in it. Or leave out the dressing that comes in a separate packet with the salad and replace it with your own. My best tip for 'pimping up' any salad is to keep some pink sea salt and balsamic vinegar (or glaze) near you, either in the car, at home or your work desk. Pink sea salt contains a higher quantity of minerals than bleached white salt. Sprinkle generously on any salad. You could even squeeze over a lemon or lime for added flavour. Add your protein on top, such as fish, beef, chicken, ham or, if plant-based, tofu or chickpeas, and enjoy.

- Why not treat yourself afterwards to a Nakd bar made with natural dates and nuts and only a hundred calories?

- If salads aren't your thing, consider vegetables. Adding vegetables to your meals is one of the best things you can do to make you feel fuller for longer without the bloat. There's a big difference between feeling full from potatoes and broccoli and the typical 'stuffed' feeling you get from eating junk food.

You may not like vegetables as an adult. You may even feel you've 'outgrown' them. You may have a vendetta against them because you hated them so much as a kid, and your parents forced you to eat them against your will. Now, as a scornful adult, the childhood trauma of your parents' good advice makes you rebel like a grumpy teenager. Whatever your stance on vegetables, as an adult, consider that it's one of the fastest ways to get healthier.

Vegetables are an excellent low-calorie nutritional option, which is wonderful if you're trying to lose weight and know you have an appetite. Fill your plate with green veg, and you're a hell of a lot less likely to want a tonne more food afterwards.

Why green vegetables? They are generally the most nutrient-dense of all the vegetables. The best sources for nutritional power are cruciferous vegetables, such as cabbage, broccoli, Brussels sprouts, kale, cauliflower, and other green, leafy vegetables. They're astonishingly dense with vitamins such as A, C and K, along with compounds that can help reduce inflammation in the body. They are also associated with a lower risk of chronic diseases such as diabetes, asthma and Alzheimer's. There is evidence that there are significantly reduced rates of many types of cancer in people who consume high amounts of cruciferous vegetables. That fact alone should be enough to get you a little more excited about eating more vegetables. Again, your life could literally depend on it.

There are so many ways to make your veg more appealing. You can steam, bake in coconut oil, pan fry, stir fry, add to soup, or cook mildly to add to your salad as extra crunch. If you're reading this and thinking, "I'm no good at cooking" (I know many adults who don't cook at all), get yourself on You-Tube for some cooking tutorials. Take your daily health more seriously by not relying on others to make all your meals. You're not a child.

Once a day, hold your head a little higher by having a personal standard of at least one big portion of salad or veg for your health. Believe me. It will go a long way. It could even contribute to you seeing your grandkids grow up.

HABIT 5 - NO FOOD TO BE CONSUMED TWO TO THREE HOURS BEFORE SLEEP

You may think you eat at the 'wrong' times. You may be right, but only when it comes to your sleep quality. Eating late at night has little to do with getting fat. It's always a matter of calories in versus calories out for weight gain or weight loss, not *when* you eat. But did you know that digesting a meal just before bed doesn't allow your body and brain to rest and reset fully? Doing this may seriously disrupt your sleep quality and hormonal balance.

You probably know you *should* get around seven to nine hours of sleep a night. While this is a ballpark figure, the actual amount you need to sleep is individual. I know people who thrive on precisely six hours of sleep, while some need nine or more hours to function. The amount of sleep you need is dependent on your stress levels, whether you're an active person doing a manual job or exercising hard, etc. The more you push yourself, the more restorative sleep you may require, as the brain and body will need further rest. Age also plays a factor.

The number of hours you need to sleep is only one factor when considering sleep quality and feeling rested and recovered the next day. Several studies[4] demonstrate it's not always down to the length of the sleep, but how many cycles you go through. These cycles determine whether your sleep is restorative. Your sleep goes through several cycles to restore and regenerate your body and brain during the night. Most of these cycles last around 90 minutes, and, on average, people tend to go through four to six cycles each night, depending on the number of hours they're asleep.

You may have found this interesting when, for example, you've woken in the night after six hours of sleep, checked your alarm and been surprised at how refreshed you feel. But then you've realised you've still got an hour till you need to be up. You drifted off for that extra hour and woken up feeling drowsy and generally worse than you did an hour earlier. Why is that? It could be that if you had six hours and felt great, you had just completed four full cycles of sleep (four 90 minute cycles). That extra hour put you in the middle of another cycle that you couldn't complete. Now you're left feeling worse as the extra hour affected your sleep quality.

Similarly, if your stomach is full before sleep and all the blood is in there trying to digest the food, it can't cycle around the brain and body as efficiently to restore and repair to maximal effect. Eating before sleeping will affect your sleep quality, whether you sleep the 'right' number of hours or not. Most people sleep better on an empty stomach, while some may benefit from a small snack an hour or so before bed. I've found the majority who eat big meals and gorge late at night have poor quality sleep and thus suffer from fatigue, irritability and lack of focus the following day.

Let's keep this as simple as possible. Have a personal standard that your last meal or food will be two to three hours before sleep to give your body a chance to digest and then fall into a restful night's sleep. If you need to consume before bed, I'd recommend simply water or a good herbal tea. The nighttime teas I love are 'Tulsi' tea and 'Yogi Bedtime Tea Soothing Caramel' (don't blame me for the crazy dreams you may have after ingesting these herbs). Make sure you have nothing calorie-dense before you sleep. The 'warm milk or Horlicks before bed to aid restful sleep' advice is a myth, just like 'breakfast is the most important meal of the day,' and you should eat your Kellogg's, Shreddies, etc. Do you know who sold you that idea? Breakfast cereal companies!

DEBUNKING THE MYTH THAT CARBS AFTER 6 PM MAKE YOU FAT

Too many calories make you fat, not just calories from carbs. Yes, carbs may make you feel bloated after eating, but that's because you overindulge as they taste so damn good. However, eating them at night could be a good thing. Let me explain.

Eating carbs (sugars) blunts or lowers cortisol levels, your 'fight or flight' stress hormone. To aid restful sleep, you want this low at night as cortisol plays a role in waking you up in the morning. Have you ever wondered why you crave sugar when you're stressed? It's because the sugar helps to lower your stress levels temporarily. In excess, sugars stress the body (overconsumption of anything isn't good for you). However, as long as you don't consume sugars excessively, the internal effect is one of calm. It could be advantageous to have some sweet potato, rice or a little pasta in the evening, with a small amount of dark chocolate (70% cocoa or more) to keep you sane and help with your sleep (allowing two to three hours for digestion before bedtime, of course).

Consuming carbs could also positively affect your body's natural circadian rhythm, which is your body's natural wake and sleep cycle. In the past, people would go to sleep when it was dark and wake when it was light. The invention of regular jobs, modern technology and the light and dark seasons make that quite difficult now, and your circadian rhythm may get messed up frequently. Carbs can be used to rebalance your circadian rhythm.

HABIT 6 - ZERO PHONE, LAPTOP OR TV 30-60 MINUTES BEFORE BED

This is especially true for having a TV inside the bedroom. Your bedroom is literally for two things only, and that's sleep and sex. That's it. There should be no tech in the bedroom. Do you find yourself scrolling in bed? Do you use the excuse of using your phone as an alarm? Put the phone on the other side of the room, so you have to get out of bed physically to turn it off. Too much technology will interfere with the two hormones that are important to your sleep patterns. You need to balance these two hormones to be able to drift into a restful night's sleep.

Melatonin at night and *serotonin* in the day are the two hormones that need to be well balanced so you can create a good sleep/wake cycle. A good morning routine with exercise, fresh air, and natural light can help naturally stimulate serotonin. You're stimulated to produce melatonin as darkness starts to fall, which usually coincides with sunset. Your brain starts releasing this chemical a few hours before you go to bed, signalling to your body that it's time to wind down.

Nowadays, staying awake with artificial lighting from a laptop or looking at a TV or phone screen can impact your natural melatonin production. The blue light emanating from your electronic devices inhibits melatonin production, confusing your body when it should be asleep or awake. Light stimulation can delay melatonin production till much later on in the evening, depriving your body of enough time to relax before you go to bed.

Serotonin is the body's happiness hormone. It's a feel-good neurotransmitter that's involved in countless bodily functions, including emotions, mood, appetite and memory, as well as sleep. While its exact role is still relatively unknown to many scientists, high serotonin levels are associated with wakefulness and lower levels with sleep. Serotonin is a precursor to melatonin. Serotonin gets to a certain level during the day then turns into melatonin which signals the brain that it's time for sleep.

As you can see, staying away from your phone, laptop or artificial light for 30-60 minutes before bed can help your body naturally calm into a more restful state. This helps your natural sleep/wake cycles.

Let's be honest. If you keep watching that next episode of that thriller boxset, if you keep scrolling through socials, checking emails late at night or getting involved in Netflix too much when you should be resting, you have to keep your tech at a distance from you. This is especially the case with phones and laptops. Unlike a phone or laptop, TV is often a better option because you're further away from the screen. A TV is often six to eight feet away, while a phone or laptop may be only one to two feet away. Therefore, TVs provide slightly less intense light stimulation. But it still could be affecting your ability to wind down in the evening.

Also, try using blue light filter glasses. I've found they help my brain feel less tired when staring for long hours at a screen, as they contain a filter that limits the amount of blue light that reaches the eye. This might also benefit long-term eye health, although not enough studies support this right now. However, with modern technology and screen time being at an all-time high, the artificial light in your screens does have a very stimulating effect on the brain. Staring at a screen for hours on end can cause brain fatigue and eye strain. Blue light glasses have been shown to help with this, and I can personally say if you're spending many hours in front of a screen, they will help limit your fatigue and make it easier on your eyes and brain.

HABIT 7 - GET TO BED AN HOUR EARLIER

As simple as this sounds, getting to bed an hour earlier helps create major discipline in your life. I know I mentioned that sleep is unique to each individual. However, a helpful coach is here to help you get into a great healthy routine. Try this. Put your phone on night shift mode in the evening, or simply dull the brightness setting. Or try putting it into aeroplane mode and leave it in another room as you wind down. This could be very useful for helping your brain become more restful in the evening. Getting an extra hour's sleep a night totalled up over one week equals seven additional hours of sleep. That's a whole night's extra sleep per week! Think of the positive effect that could have on your mental health and physical performance.

Be truthful. After 9 PM, what happens that you can't catch up on the next day? If your nightclubbing days are over, you can catch any movie or TV show on-demand the next day. Post 9 PM, all you're doing is tempting yourself to enter and stay in the 'beer and takeaway zone.' You'll *never* regret getting to bed earlier.

But hey, if you currently wake up rested, happy and full of beans, you can probably ignore this. However, if you struggle to get up and get started in the mornings, this is for sure one habit you need to start employing as soon as you can. How about tonight?

SUMMARY

All habits are not equal. Taking you through all seven habits, each of which is super valuable towards energising your daily life, you may find you get more benefit from one habit than another. However, they are all interrelated, and you'll find when you do the habits that you get the most from, these will help you achieve the other habits more easily.

As shown in Figure 9 (Pie Chart of Healthy Balance) at the start of this chapter, if you just drink the recommended amount of water and get to bed an hour earlier, you'll notice some great results. But if you leave out the training or exercise part, you're missing out on a whole host of positive emotions and benefits, such as sticking to the big-ass salad. Eating vegetables is easier once you train (sweat, move, etc.) because your brain likes to follow up on good behaviour and not spoil hard work.

The brain loves ticking off a completed task. Just like scrolling through your phone, when you tick off a small achievement, you get that dopamine hit, that feel-good chemical in your brain that gets you coming back for more. So don't forget to mark down your efforts to help with your accountability. The best way to do this is to download and print out my Seven Daily Habits Personal Checklist (use the QR code at the beginning of this chapter) so that you can tick each habit off daily.

In the next chapter, I will go into how to keep going, no matter what happens, so that when you have momentum, there's nothing to stop you in your tracks.

CHAPTER 3

HOW TO KEEP GOING

When you start something new, it's always quite exciting. The uncertainty is a fresh new flavour that you're eager to try out. After all, variety is the spice of life. This is why starting is often the easiest part. However, keeping going and being consistent is the biggest challenge for most. Staying consistent brings the most significant results, not just starting or trying something new.

In this chapter, I'm going to delve deep into how to keep going, no matter what happens, but also understand why you keep stopping and what you can do about it.

THE CYCLE OF MOTIVATION

Do you have the following traits?

You start on Monday, somewhat motivated. You need to burn off all the calories you consumed after a heavy weekend. You feel tired but know you need to sort yourself out. Therefore, you start your diet and even attend the gym. Monday goes well. On Tuesday, you have the same lunch and feel more energised after a good sleep on Monday night. Then comes Wednesday. It's midweek, and you start to feel a slump. You forgot your lunch, so you grab a sandwich or something quick from the local cafe or shop. It momentarily fills you up, but you don't feel as 'on it' anymore. Thursday comes, and you didn't prepare your work lunch. So you go for convenience once again. You missed the gym last night, and you're aware it's Friday tomorrow. You think, "Ah, I'll just start again on Monday."

Does this sound familiar? Of course, it does. This will be the millionth time you've said and done this. I speak to hundreds of people a year who are in the exact same position. Every weekend is usually their downfall. They live in a vicious cycle. Most of the year, people live in these cycles, finding a few weeks here and there, usually January after Christmas and July before the summer holidays, where they're seriously focused and 'on it.' This is because they feel guilty that they've eaten like an idiot for months beforehand, and they feel fat and crap about themselves. But then, after another few weeks of being 'on it', they drop back into this cycle of, "I'll start on Monday," or, "I need motivation."

Regardless of the specifics, the story is mostly the same. Most people are 'start-stop' people. They're always starting on Monday and failing or falling off every weekend. Why is this?

First of all, let's look at how people are conditioned regarding their weekends. Since early school days, we've all been taught that weekends are days off from normality. It's time to do what you like and indulge in as much as you want before getting back to 'normal.' That's ok while you're a teenager. As adults, however, in a regular Monday to Friday job, you continue with this mindset. Since you work hard during the week, you deserve to treat yourself at the weekend, correct?

However, I need you to ask yourself a few questions. What is a treat to you? A Sunday dinner and two pints of alcohol with family? A takeaway curry on Saturday night with a movie? A bottle of wine and a pizza on a Friday night? Coffee and naughty cake while out shopping on Saturday? A bacon sandwich or a full English breakfast on Saturday morning? Or is it all of the above, but in larger quantities?

We can all be greedy pigs at times. I know I can. Hell, I've consumed over 10,000 calories in drink and food on several weekends during my 20s. But as we get older, we have to start considering our health and understanding balance.

BALANCE

Balance isn't getting wasted every weekend. It's not about having a crappy diet from Friday night until Monday morning and then expecting that being healthy for the rest of the week will even the score. You know, deep down, after a heavy weekend, you're not feeling 100% right till at least Tuesday, and sometimes even midweek.

Here are some hard facts. If you waste every weekend a year, that's 52 weekends. That's the equivalent of 104 days. That's a whole quarter of your year wasted. Imagine looking back and thinking, "I'm so glad I felt like shit almost every weekend." It's utter madness.

To combat this, why not make Sunday your Monday? Or start tracking your calories on a Friday (like we do at TST). Why not get up on a Saturday at 6 AM to train, sweat or move? That's what our TST guys do to make sure they stay on track at the weekend.

Hey, I'm not Scrooge here, sucking out all the fun from your life. You may love going out for a drink, and you may adore the feeling of being intoxicated and being gluttonous with your food. And that's ok, now and again. But if your life isn't looking the way you want it to, if you hate your body and your health and energy is suffering, you've got to start making some new choices, especially surrounding your rules about your weekends.

Here are a few ideas on new perspectives for the weekend:

- Start on Sunday.
- Consider Friday and Sunday nights as 'school nights' (weeknights).
- Make Saturday morning just like a Monday morning.
- Allow yourself just one treat meal on one weekend evening (Friday *or* Saturday, not both).
- Only drink once, maximum twice a month (only on a Saturday evening).
- Leave the Whatsapp group, which includes friends who only see you when you drink.
- Track your calorie intake only at the weekend (for extra clarity).

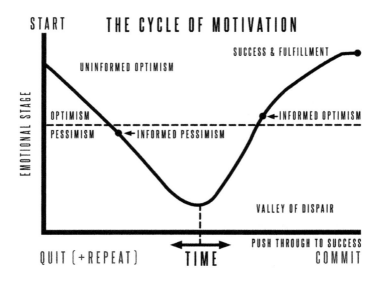

Figure 10: Cycle Of Motivation Diagram

Figure 10 is a visual representation of the Cycle of Motivation. Most people find themselves falling into this cycle throughout their lives. It's a trap that seems neverending. Let's look into further detail and what happens when you start something new.

As you can see in Figure 10, at the start, your results feel pretty high, as is your optimism. Just starting something can make you feel good, right? You've made a decision, you're now 'on it', and you've committed. You're getting praise and feeling better about yourself for taking action. You have what is called uninformed optimism. You're not quite sure exactly what to expect, how long it'll go on for or what will happen. However, you're open-minded, you've begun your journey, and you feel good about your decision.

As time goes on, your results may improve a little. You feel good for a while, and you're on track. But then things start to slow down, and you feel yourself or your results beginning to slide. What happens here, as you can see in the diagram, is you start to discover a little more of what to expect and what's truly involved in the process. This is called informed pessimism.

This causes self-doubt to creep in where you start to realise it's not all easy or fun. You're finding it, at times, more challenging than enjoyable. You begin to feel, "What's the point?" Your brain starts to think, "Holy shit, you mean I have to go to the gym even at the weekend? Do you mean I can't eat that when everyone else can? Do you mean I have to get up earlier every Monday? Do you mean I have to do this even when I'm this tired? Do you mean I can't have that cream cake today? But it's 'cream cake Thursday' in the office!"

See where I'm going here? You're now further informed about what's really expected of you to get results. I'm using health and fitness as an example here, but this is relevant to any challenging venture. As your pessimism sets in, you feel your results start to fade because of the greater clarity of the ongoing process. And, of course, results do slow down in most cases at some point. Then you'll sink into what is known as the Valley of Despair.

It's make-or-break time. You've focused on the process for a while, showing up and doing the work. However, nothing much seems to be happening any-more. You've been following the plan but can't see much change. You think it's not working, so you decide, "I'm spending all this money and time for nothing. It's getting me nowhere. I'm just going to quit, drop out and start again when I've got less going on. I've just lost my motivation!"

You quit. Guess what? You feel the pressure is off. You feel relieved now no one's going to ask you any more questions. You can eat what you want, and you don't have to think about it anymore. You can get on with other items on your to-do list and chill out every night after work. And you feel alright for a while.

Then, somewhere down the line, you start feeling lousy again. You feel tired, ratty, and unfit. You're wearing baggier clothes to hide your body, and you're having to buy bigger sizes because you stopped what you were doing. You try to justify it in your head, so you start again with something new. You're all excited, ready and motivated for your new venture. You're uninformed about what's to come, but you don't care. You just know you need to do something once again.

You begin. Your initial results are high, so you feel good. A few weeks in, and it's, "Ah, it's my uncle's birthday." You end up getting 'trashed' on Saturday night, so you don't get out of bed till 2 PM on Sunday. You order a McDonald's delivery and spend the whole day in front of Netflix. You even consider ringing in sick on Monday. And you're expected to get up for the gym at 5:45 AM? Yeah, right!

You sleep in, and you're late for work. You're back in that Valley of Despair. You think, "Ah, what's the point in this? I just can't focus at the minute. I've got a lot going on." So you consider quitting. "I think I'll drop out, come back to it when I've got less going on."

A conversation comes up at lunchtime this particular Monday. James in the office asks you, "Another hefty weekend, mate?" You respond with, "Yeah mate, I'm hanging" (suffering from too much alcohol intake). Then, James tells you what you need to hear. "You need to sort yourself out, mate. You keep saying this all the time, but you're still fat. You keep stuffing your face, getting more and more unhealthy and complaining all the time about it. You always find money to get pissed and buy crap food, but you're not doing anything about your health."

His remark triggers you. "Cheeky bastard!" But then, after a couple of minutes, you finally realise, "He's got a point. I'm always living in this vicious cycle. I'm always tired, and I'm getting pretty sick of my bullshit." You decide you're ready to start again. You need to smarten up and take a different route from the previous attempts. And that's to commit to the process. You text your personal trainer and say, "Could you possibly fit me in tonight to train and give me a kick up the arse? I'm sick of my own bullshit. I need the extra push." You decide to commit instead of quit. You invest money into yourself rather than 'piss it up the wall.'

Look again at Figure 10 (Cycle of Motivation Diagram). Once you commit, you may not see results instantly, but you see a steady improvement. After committing while *in* the Valley of Despair, that little extra push when you're about to throw in the towel brings you up. You start to reinvent yourself, feel your self-esteem rise and finally have the whole weekend 'off the drink' (without alcohol). You even get up at 5:45 AM on a Saturday and do your training. Your confidence this week is the highest it's been in months because you decided to commit to yourself instead of quitting like you always did before when it got hard.

At first, the truth hurts, but it sets you free. Thank God for people like James telling it to you straight. Even though quitting seems like the easy option, a little extra commitment, a little more time and a little more effort, just as you're about to give up, goes a long way. Don't forget this cycle. Remember 'what James said' and decide carefully when you want to quit.

WHAT HAPPENED TO SCOTT? (CASE STUDY)

Figure 11: Scott Ryan Transformation

This is Scott Ryan, the only man ever to win our TST Tribesman of the Month award twice. These photos are two years apart, and they blow my mind. Yes, you read that right. This isn't some 12-week transformation where the person gets fat again after losing weight before a holiday or wedding. You can't change your life long term in six weeks. It takes time to develop lifestyle habits that stick. Sometimes it can take years. That's the truth no one wants to hear.

Here's Scott's story, in his own words:

"I was told that my turnaround was some sort of midlife crisis. It was a realisation that, while on the surface I identified myself as a happy 'work hard play hard' type of person, in reality, I knew deep down I wasn't living my best life, and my mental and physical health projected that. I spent most of my day justifying the state I was in by making excuses. I was 'too busy,' 'too fat,' 'too old,' or 'too stressed.' I'd temporarily start to turn things around, but then that 'bitch voice' in my head would win with more excuses. "I have an injury," "It's too cold," "It's raining," or "I've life dramas to deal with."

In April, I started my first challenge, adopting a 'no excuse' lifestyle for 75 days, sticking to a routine and doing what I said I would do. I struggled for the first few weeks. It then clicked that this new routine was so much more rewarding, simple, and less exhausting than constantly making excuses. I lost 34lb in the first two and a half months.

It was great, but to be honest, it became boring. On the last day of the challenge, I received a message out of nowhere from Luke, asking how I was doing. I explained my progress, and then he asked, "What's next?" There was no excuse not to rejoin the Tribe. Three months later, I'd lost another 42lb (19kg). Yes, that's just in the last three months.

The support of being surrounded every other day by people with a positive mindset is incredible. Every training is an example of people turning up and working around excuses, injuries, and chasing their personal goals at all levels. The accountability, variety, and having Luke just a message away for instant advice is invaluable. The weight loss is rewarding, and I feel great.

The most rewarding part of this is how my actions have changed my identity. I can see my kids learning by the 'no excuse' example this old man is sharing with them. I still have loads of work to do and improvements to make, but I'm excited."

-Scott 'What's Next?' Ryan

TWO QUICK STEPS TO FIXING YOUR START–STOP MENTALITY

Do you ever get mad at yourself, judge yourself harshly and quit things too quickly because you feel you lack skill or talent in that area? Only to try again and find it's ok for a while. But then you find yourself back into the cycle I talked about previously. I want to expand on this because it's too valuable to leave out. I will give you two things to help change your habitual ways regarding your start-stop mentality. These are:

- language (what you say)
- attitude (how you approach things)

1. Stop saying, "I'll try," or, "I'll do my best."

Your language and what you say to yourself is critical. Every time you say "I'll try" to do something, you're giving yourself an easy way out. They're nice, easy things to say in response to a new challenge that you feel you won't be very good at doing. Think back to when you last said this phrase or heard someone else say it. I'd imagine the tone of voice was one of uncertainty. It was possibly low pitched and unenthusiastic, like someone verbally 'sighing.' Perhaps the person's gaze was directed downwards as they said it?

You'll notice from now on how your body language changes with phrases that you say out loud. The body language of looking down with a slightly lower pitched tone does not scream confidence, does it? Yoda from Star Wars said it best when he said, "Do or do not. There is no try." This is old-school 1970s wisdom from a Hollywood movie, but damn, it contains some cold hard truth!

Either bloody do it, with all you've got, with every ounce of you. Or don't. If you fail in your attempts, that's ok. If you don't want to do it, just have the guts to say, "No." At least there's some certainty in that, and you're not half-arsed (half-assed for my American friends) about your decision and giving yourself an easy cop-out.

Conner McGregor (a famous mixed martial artist) said, "I'll win, or I'll learn," in response to the media asking about his mindset before upcoming fights against people he'd never faced before in the UFC (Ultimate Fighting Championship). Do you think McGregor would ever say, "I'll do my best," or, "I'll try," in preparation for his fights? Hell no! The guy's response was simple. "I'll win, or I'll learn." That's confidence. That's doing it and not just trying.

Whenever you catch yourself saying, "I'll do my best," remember the movie The Rock with Nicholas Cage and Sean Connery. There's a scene where the war veteran Connery gives Cage a gun as they're about to embark on a dangerous mission. When he hands over the weapon, Connery says, "You sure you're ready for this?" Cage responds, "I'll do my best." Sean Connery stops for a moment, looks him dead in the eyes and says, "Your best? Losers always whine about their best. Winners go home and fuck the prom queen."

Don't be a loser with loser language, such as, "I'll try," or, "I'll do my best." Believe me. Loser language will enter your head as a typical response to most uncertain situations. But, instead of letting it take over, change your language to approach the problem with a little more confidence. Why not say something like, "I got this!" Or how about, "Ok, let's do this!" You'll feel more self-control and self-belief.

Think about your body language when you say these words. It's much more assertive and confident. You'll likely say these words while looking into the other person's eyes (true confidence). In addition, you're likely to have a taller posture, less hunched shoulders, and a more assertive voice tone. You also may notice a distinct nod of the head to confirm the strong decision.

If you've heard others say these words or said them yourself, you'll notice these subtle shifts in physiology, which contribute to higher levels of self-belief and confidence to help keep you going. Be careful what you say. Your language matters.

2. **Don't get angry, get M.A.D. (your attitude and how you approach things).**

Your attitude and approach are equally as important as what you say to yourself. If you get frustrated, beat yourself up and self-sabotage your results regularly, I'm encouraging you to get M.A.D. which stands for:

- Must
- Act
- Determined

When you get angry, you throw your toys out of the pram and think, "Sod it!" You reach for the immediately gratifying choices that give you a quick fix, like porn, gambling, food, drink, cigarettes, etc. Why not channel that energy more constructively?

Getting mad can be very effective if you direct the energy appropriately. Rather than being uncontrollably aggressive, lashing out, snappy, eating food or drinking alcohol to make you feel better, why not feel that energy inside you and *act* determined. When you're feeling a bit hotheaded, ask yourself, "What's the most useful action I can take right now to help me progress?"

It could be that you just need some fresh air and go for a walk without your phone. It could be that you need a workout. You may need to listen to music for five to ten minutes with some headphones while sitting in a chair. You may just need a nap. You may need to write a list of everything that's bothering you. Rather than have it in your head, write it all down, confront each one by one, and then cross it off. Remember, the brain loves crossing things off a list.

When stress starts building up in your body, you'll often feel tightness in your chest, maybe a knot in your stomach or even experience lower back pain and tightness.

TASK: BREATHING EXERCISE

Try this as you're reading this book. Stretch open your chest. Now pin your shoulders back, breathe deeply in through your nose, physically push out your belly as you fill it with air, and then breathe out through your mouth slowly for four to six seconds. Go on. No one's watching you.

Repeat this exercise, but breathe in deeper and fill more of your belly and chest this time. Now breathe out through your mouth even slower than before. Take a good few seconds to exhale. There's no rush. One last time, breathe in very slowly, fill your belly, your chest and now into your neck and head, sucking in that last bit of air through your mouth if needed. You'll feel two inches taller at this point. Then *slowly* exhale that stress for 15 seconds and just pause a second.

Next time your stress levels are high and your anxiety gets ahead of you, remember this breathing technique and practice it throughout the day. You'll begin to notice, almost immediately, the physical relaxation in your midsection and the immediate calmness that deep breathing provides. And remember, don't lose control, get M.A.D instead.

Don't forget the famous Zig Ziglar quote, "Your attitude determines your altitude." Nothing can stop you from achieving your goals when you have the right mental attitude. The most recent tattoo on my wrist in 2021 has the words 'attitude is everything,' opposite Stone Cold Steve Austin, reminding me that a badass wouldn't lose his mind at the first sign of stress. He'd tackle it and handle it.

EIGHT POWERFUL SYSTEMS TO SUPPORT YOURSELF

1. ROUTINE

Daily, weekly and monthly routines are critical to helping you keep going. Most people fail consistently because their routine is simply not beneficial for where they say they want to go.

You develop your routine by consistent repetition of habits. You have habits, which you label as good or bad. You perform most of your perceived bad habits because they keep you comfortable and certain. After all, everything you do has a perceived benefit and a perceived drawback if you don't do it, as explained earlier in Chapter 1. Even if you believe that your habits are bad, you'll always do what you think will benefit you. Remember, this is true even if you label the behaviour as self-sabotage. You're still getting something from the habit or behaviour, such as certainty or even excitement in some form.

The problem most people have with changing their routine is their unguided, relentless pursuit to *stop* bad habits. Most people don't think of replacing a bad habit with a good one. Therefore, when a bad habit is absent from your routine that keeps you safe and certain, you're going to look elsewhere to try and get that fix. This is why you'll often go straight back to the behaviour you're familiar with or find another bad habit to fill the void.

The more you replace bad habits with good ones, and the more consistently you apply these good habits, the more you rewire the brain for higher self-worth. It becomes difficult to stop if you're not replacing a behaviour with something more useful. This is why most people who go cold turkey often 'cave' (give up) because there's nothing to give them an alternative feeling that is equally, if not more, satisfying.

Your brain isn't designed to keep you excited or even happy. It's wired to keep you alive, constantly looking for threats and assessing your environment. If you're unsure of something, your brain won't like that. It's why getting rid of bad habits is no easy feat. The seven daily habits explained in Chapter 2 are perfect examples of beneficial and good habits that, when applied, can help overcome and replace bad habits in many areas. They'll provide a lot of great feelings that will keep you excited, certain and enjoying the process. If you think about the habits you currently do on autopilot right now, they don't require much motivation, do they? That's because habits are just repetitions of things you've become comfortable doing again and again.

When you replace one of your bad habits with a good one for long enough, the motivation for the new habit diminishes. It'll become something that you just *do* without much thought. You'll perform them unconsciously without the need for motivation or willpower. Imagine how powerful that could be in your life.

2. PLANNING

You've heard the cliche, "Fail to plan, plan to what? Fail!" Although most people roll their eyes at phrases like this, there's truth in them that gets overlooked. There is tremendous value in having a clearly written plan or at least some focused actions written down to execute regularly.

Get more organised if you want to be less stressed.

The problem I see with most people trying to help themselves do better is remembering everything in their heads. They never use pen and paper or a journal, diary or planner to organise things. I'll say this with absolute certainty. Get more organised if you want to be less stressed.

Also, don't prioritise others over yourself. I see so many people do this. They say, "I'll have to do this for him. Then I need to go there for her. Then he needs that. Then they need me to do this." Before you know it, you've been a people pleaser for 20 years and have no energy for anything else. To help you avoid prioritising others before yourself, repeat the following sentence. There is nothing more important than me feeling good.

But to get this perspective embedded into your brain, you've got to schedule your priorities. What is a priority for you? I hope you'll say, "Health, energy and happiness." You have to *make* time for your health. It needs to be your number one priority. *Make* time to eat a proper meal and for training, walking, gym, etc., every day. Your life literally depends on it.

This is where the power of a morning routine becomes evident. Doing things before the rest of the world gets up so you can have a little bit of 'you time.' Everyone still gets 24 hours a day, whether rich, poor, fat, thin, successful, old or young. We all get the same time allocated every single day. It's how we manage it that matters, not how much time we actually have.

Your routine is your routine. You get to make it your own and do things that work for you at times that suit you. Make it work. Do yourself a favour. Next time you find yourself saying, "I don't have time for that," just take a breath and say, "I need to make time for that." Or if you're not prepared to, just say, "I'm not prepared to make time for that." At least that's accepting responsibility and not blaming something pathetic like time (we all get the same amount).

Your plan is critical to your success, whether that's daily, weekly, monthly or even yearly. You'll only progress as far as you plan. Most successful millionaires have plans that stretch three, five, or even ten years into the future. However, to start, consider daily and weekly plans to keep you accountable and less stressed. Get a simple diary or journal to keep track of your time, and use your phone calendar to schedule and keep track of where you should be. Don't do it in your head, as you'll suffer anxiety and overwhelm.

A physical means to plan and schedule is critical to keeping your head right and focused moving forward. I use my Supercharged Daily Planner, which has a great set of morning and evening questions to guide my focus, and a daily and weekly plan to keep me on track. I use it every day and would be lost without it. Keep your daily planner, journal or diary as close to you as your water bottle. Make it so you'd be lost without it.

3. ACCOUNTABILITY

"I know it sounds like I'm making excuses, but (excuse given)." How many times have you said that? One of the main reasons you would pay a coach, mentor, team or program is to keep you accountable. To make sure you were doing what you said you would do when you said you would. Not Monday. Not when you feel like it. Now.

It's too easy to put stuff off when there's no accountability. There's no one asking questions, no one checking in, and no one asking you for an update. It's too easy to say 'later' without someone or a group of people on your back, correct?

You probably already know this. But you should always be searching for someone or something to hold you accountable to a higher standard, no matter what your personal goal is. You shouldn't hide away and stick to what's comfortable and easy as that eventually leaves you feeling so far behind that quitting seems like the only option.

4. YOUR ENVIRONMENT / PEER GROUP / COMMUNITY

This is where the most decisive accountability lies. For example, if you're always hanging out with people who drink a lot of alcohol, what activity do you think you're held accountable for doing every weekend? Your community is your prime influence, and if you find you're not where you want to be in life, and you're hanging around with six losers all the time, chances are you'll always be the seventh.

You need to upgrade your environment, peer group and the community with whom you spend most of your time. I'm not saying you need to get rid of your friends or negative family members. But you can decide how much of your time you spend with them. Remember, we all get 24 hours, and we all get to choose how we allocate our 24 hours.

The power of a peer group is unquestionable. You'll always be influenced by who you hang around with the most. It's how my TST members stay so consistent with their results and efforts regarding daily high energy, fitness and health. It's because they're not alone, and they know they're held accountable for sticking to a great morning routine. You're never alone when you have a peer group that you regularly hang around with, even if that group is online. Consider how you could be around new people who would hold you to a higher standard than you'd hold yourself. For almost everyone, self-accountability just doesn't work with big things such as changing a lifestyle, mindset or achieving a big personal goal. We all need a kick up the arse from time to time and group support along the way, even me. That's why I invest in many different courses, coaches and mentors.

5. THE NEXT MEAL

This links in nicely with my topic on accountability. I'd love to raise a point here about the most important meal of the day. Most people believe breakfast is the most important meal. I've already revealed that breakfast cereal companies spread this information. They also said breakfast was a good idea for weight loss!

They want you to buy their products regularly. Many years ago, they used this phrase in their advertising.[5] Is it any wonder that you've grown up believing this is true? Your parents said it, and you heard it time and time again, so it must be true, right? In some cases, it may be true. Many people need something in their stomachs in the morning to function better. However, others get great results by fasting at breakfast.

The truth is, the most important meal of the day is simply the *next* one. The most important sleep of the week is the next one. The most important workout of the week is the next one. Do you see where I'm going here?

In terms of accountability, this message is simple. If you fall off the wagon on Thursday or Friday night, stop beating yourself up

> *Get straight back on it with the next opportunity, whenever that may be. Always think in terms of 'the next one.'*

thinking you're a failure and then waiting until Monday to eat healthy again. Wake up on Saturday, work out and have a healthy breakfast.

6. WATCH YOUR LANGUAGE

You can't build on 'shit.' "This is shit!" "I'm shit." "That's shit." "It's all shit, isn't it?" Perhaps you use these phrases regularly, or you may hear them come up in conversation. Let's be honest here. It's far too easy to call things shit. The problem with this negative perspective is that what you say aloud genuinely affects your mood and external reality. It affects how you see things. It's a very negative perspective to brand so many things shit, especially yourself. Judging your early efforts in something you feel you're not skilled at as shit or crap is far more destructive to your mental health than you realise.

Consider Figure 12 for a moment.

Figure 12: Bricklayer Laying 'Shit' Cement

A bricklayer is hard at work, building a wall to erect a house. He's mixing his cement, running the trowel over the bricks, and levelling them up to build his wall. Then he notices that the bricks don't seem secure. They don't seem to be setting. So he tries smearing another brick with cement and pressing it firmly onto another brick. He then lifts it off to see if there's any stick, only to find he's smearing his bricks with actual shit. He thinks, "This shit doesn't stick!"

He's right. Shit is bad cement, and trying to build a good solid life on shit never works. You simply can't have a happy and fulfilling life if your life is held together by shit thinking. The point I'm trying to make here is about your own 'shit' self-talk. If you're building on a foundation of shit and expecting good things to stick, you're deluding yourself. It's an easy downward spiral. As everyone else talks about how shit things are, or how shit they think they are at certain things, then yes, you can gain connection through 'shit talk.' But when it comes to empowering yourself, you must observe and be aware of how you talk to yourself.

For most people, it's just 'shit,' and that's it. There's no solution to the problem. There's just complaint after complaint. But what if you choose not to see it as a shit day. Perhaps it's been:

- a character-building day
- a challenging day
- a testing day
- a demanding day
- a new day of opportunity
- a pressing day
- a unique day
- a valuable life lesson kind of day

You should grow through the shit you go through, but that's only possible if you start choosing to see things a different way. Watch your language. You're always in control of what you say.

7. DATA OVER DRAMA

Another important point about accountability is having new ways to measure it. There's no perfect way for everyone, but the only way to know whether you're progressing or not is to measure it. Gather the facts, not just the impressions of what you *think* is happening.

Several years ago, I was introduced to this fascinating concept of 'data over drama.' This asks what the facts are of your situation and the measurables. There's more than one way to measure. Take weight loss, for example. Let's use Jacky, a 37-year-old female overweight by 2st (12.7kg). She's in a regular exercise routine, three times a week, and tries to eat healthily. She gets on her bathroom scales about once every other day and just can't stop self-sabotaging when things don't go how she expects.

She gets a little happy when she sees a pound come off on the scales on Friday morning, so she indulges with wine and takeaways all weekend. She then gets back on the scales on Monday morning only to see she's put on 3lb (1.4kg) and is *devastated*. She's upset because the number on the scales didn't go down. She's almost crying, deeply humiliated, and thinks, "What's the point? This is ridiculous. Why do I even bother?" Her entire self-worth depends upon a device showing a specific number.

This is a classic example of drama over data. She may not have lost weight, according to her bathroom scales. However, she's only considering one minor point of data and allowing her own drama (feelings) to override any other possible results she may be getting from the process. If you relate to Jacky here, consider one of the following while trying to lose weight or get in shape:

- Have your waist and hip measurements changed?
- How much better do your clothes feel now?
- How much better do you breathe?
- How much has your energy improved?
- How do you handle stress now compared to before?
- How much have you cut down on your drinking habit?
- How much better are you sleeping?
- How much more are you getting done during the day?
- Are your kids now seeing you make more of an effort with your health?

- How much stronger do you feel in your core? Perhaps you can hold a longer plank time?
- How much fitter do you feel?
- How much more 'lifted' has your general mood been?
- How much more consistent have you been with your general efforts?
- How many more compliments are you getting (even if you brush them off)?
- How fewer excuses do you now make compared to usual?
- How has your relationship with food improved?
- How much more muscle do you physically feel within your body?
- How much more active are you day-to-day?
- How many fewer takeaways are you consuming during the month?

Nothing in the above list mentions scales. There are zero electronic devices dictating happiness and measuring progress. It's easy to see how often someone can get hooked on just one point of data. They over analyse to the point where they're utterly blind to so many other points that could potentially keep them going. These points could switch their emotions in minutes, from devastated to proud and roaring, ready for the next challenge. There are more benefits to a great health routine than they realise, especially when they are so obsessed with just one particular outcome and fixed in their expectations of how things *should* work.

Never deny the power in different points of data. It's all valuable. This is why tracking and writing down as many data points as possible is so beneficial to your progress and, ultimately, your happiness. For example, writing down and marking how you feel out of ten each day, how much water you drank, how many training sessions you made last month, how many times you added vegetables to a meal, how many little wins you had yesterday, etc.

Don't pile your self worth on one point of data and allow your drama to over-rule you. More data equals less drama and a better perspective.

8. HONEST ASSESSMENT

There's a lot of well-intentioned advice along the lines of, "Never look back," or, "Always look where you're going." While I agree that your attitude determines your altitude and your trajectory, without looking back to take an honest assessment, you'll keep making the same mistakes over and over. You'll always get pulled back from real progress and momentum. Take as many data points as you can along your journey. They will help you look back with a better perspective.

WEEKLY REVIEW

At the end of each week, I review my life in general. I ask myself some persuasive questions to steer my mind in the right direction. No matter how challenging or tiring the week may have been, I do my assessment period every Sunday at 7 AM. I do this in bed, alongside my 'missus,' some speciality coffee and our three cats, Milly, Betsy and Toffee-toes. This is where my partner and I write down our top five weekly wins. Our best or favourite moments, which range from big wins like signing up five new clients to a program, lifting my heaviest weight in the gym, or spending another five hours on my book, to smaller wins such as sex happened twice, drinking the most water this week, or got to bed on time six nights out of seven, etc.

You may have heard this before. If you can't appreciate the small things regularly, how are you supposed to appreciate the big things fully? Reflecting on the week with an optimistic attitude works wonders, rather than just branding it 'shit' and just hoping the next week gets better. This proactive approach builds far more momentum, pushing you into the new week ahead.

Alongside writing down your biggest wins of the week, it's vital to assess what went wrong. What has been the biggest lesson you learned? What could you do to improve this coming week? Writing all of this down helps your mind focus on solutions to problems rather than dwelling on negative thought patterns that drive you further down into the ground.

Your review doesn't need to be perfect. You just need to be consistent with your quantity of execution, i.e., just do it over and over again. It also means being honest with your answers, even if you can't find much to be proud or excited about or you're feeling negative. This actively steers your mind into the week ahead with optimism. It's just being a little more organised to reduce your stress and dramatically increase your self-worth. Why wouldn't you want to do that?

Ask yourself, and write down the answers to the following questions at the end of each week on Sunday morning:

1. What was my total phone screen time this week? Find this in the settings of your smartphone.

2. What were my top five biggest wins this week? No matter how small they may feel, anything can be big to you.

3. What further action will I take for each win to keep up the momentum?

4. What was the thing or subject I complained about most this week?

5. What were my top three biggest disappointments this week?

6. What are the three things I'll do to improve on these this coming week?

7. What is the biggest lesson I've learned about myself or my life this week?

As you can imagine, a weekly honest assessment of as much data as you can gather will drastically improve your mindset going into the following week. This is a basic self-assessment and is super effective. Over time, you can start to self-assess in more detail. But, for now, answer these seven questions with pen and paper. Do this every week and increase the frequency of this great habit.

SUMMARY

To keep going and stay motivated, you must be:

- real
- honest
- accountable

You can't continue self-sabotaging your efforts and expect to be progressing with momentum. As I discussed earlier, self-sabotage or beating yourself up is *not* useful, and yet you're getting a benefit from it, such as certainty. Otherwise, you wouldn't do it. You always do things that in some way benefit you. When you hide away, avoid the hard work, or put yourself in a guilty or shameful position, you're often just protecting yourself from further vulnerability or exposure.

Remember, you're always doing what you believe has the most benefit and value. If you see enough benefit in performing a particular behaviour and enough drawbacks to avoiding that behaviour, you'll always behave that way. When you see enough drawbacks to doing that behaviour and enough benefits to avoiding that behaviour, you'll always do something else instead.

If you want new results, and I know you do, you've got to start implementing new strategies. Change your perspective, watch your language, get real and honestly assess yourself. Plan, review and always seek accountability from someone or some*thing*.

You've now discovered the basic framework for a new mindset and some seriously healthy habits. You'll learn more techniques in the upcoming chapters. One thing that crushes ongoing progress is your belief about comfort zones. The next chapter is the shortest one in the book. I've designed it specifically to help you see your comfort zone in a different light. So let's shift that perspective.

CHAPTER 4

HOW TO BE COMFORTABLE WITH BEING UNCOMFORTABLE

The problem I see with so many people trying to make a big change in their lives, whether with their health, job, lifestyle, relationship, etc., is that they end up trying to do too much at once. They step too far into discomfort and then realise they can't keep it up alongside everything else they're doing. They get so overwhelmed with their decision that they end up eventually just falling back into what's comfortable for them.

The real secret to long-lasting change is to do mildly uncomfortable things frequently rather than scaring yourself to death with every new challenge. Many gurus will talk about a *radical* shift or *massive* action. While that's not bad advice, most people end up getting caught up in the moment, making a big decision in a state of high energy without thinking about it, only to find they simply can't keep up the routine of their 'massive' action.

I see this all too often, and while I think making a big scary decision can be very useful for changing your habits longer-term, massive action and radical shifts usually don't stick. This is why so many people fall off the wagon and let themselves go too frequently. A radical shift could be a complete 180-degree turn. It's a little like when people meet a new partner, move in after three months, get married after six, have a kid after a year, change their job and stop seeing their friends altogether. They then wonder why they're more stressed, tired, angry and out of shape than ever just a year later.

If you rush into things too quickly without adequate time to readjust, you end up living your life to please others. You're also likely to end up hating your own life and ignoring your health and the things that make you happy just because you're caught up in the whole emotion of it all. I'm sure you agree, you're not useful to anyone if you're tired, angry, out of shape and miserable with your life.

People have this tendency to rush into things. An example is deciding to crash diet for the next six weeks and train five days a week at the gym for a holiday, wedding or important event when you haven't been dieting or regularly going to the gym at all. They get these ideas, often influenced by Instagram or Facebook or what someone else is doing, and they think they need to do the same.

I'd like you to consider your life-changing results to be like a prescription. Although it could be the same as another person's, your prescription would always be what the doctor believed would help you with your specific problem. Are you always a start-stop, all-or-nothing, going from one thing to the next kind of person? Do you try to take massive action by pushing well out of your comfort zone and expect it to be a long-term change? You're kidding yourself.

Instead of shifting your life by 180 degrees, pushing you so far out of your comfort zone that you're terrified, try thinking about it differently. Instead of it shifting in big angles, think about it shifting in small degrees. Try shifting one, two or three degrees at a time so that you're mildly uncomfortable and stretching yourself, but not so far that you're terrified.

Most people go overboard too quickly and try to be intense, like the people they see online, and they try to get results as fast as possible. Nothing, and I mean nothing, will beat consistency over intensity for long-term results.

> *Nothing, and I mean nothing, will beat consistency over intensity for long-term results.*

Consistency over intensity should be your new way of thinking. Not how fast you can go, but more how far you can go. Just stay consistent.

COMFORT ZONE VS COMFORT BUBBLE

You will have heard people say, "Step outside of your comfort zone," or, "Take a leap of faith." While I love this kind of advice, as I mentioned previously, most people tend to gravitate back towards what's convenient and comfortable for them. After all, we're creatures of habit.

Consider Figure 13:

Figure 13: Comfort Zone Diagram

Think for a second about your comfort zone, as shown by the thick black rectangle in Figure 13. You'll know where you're comfortable and feel most competent and familiar. Most days, you'll operate at 80–90% plus in that area. While stepping outside of your comfort zone can help challenge and stretch you, it's also terrifying. Most people are not ready to step into unfamiliar territory, so they end up going back to what they know, which is the familiar zone of comfort.

Let's look at your comfort zone in a different, useful way. Consider your zone of comfort as not a zone but a bubble. Don't look at it as a fixed square box that confines you, leaving you scared or apprehensive about stepping out of its rigid edges. Instead, visualise it as a comfort bubble around you. Think of Sonic the Hedgehog on the old Sega Mega Drive console when he gets his invincibility bubble around him!

Now, imagine you're able to stretch that bubble from within, to make it wider with more of your efforts while still feeling comfortable and familiar. The more you stretch your bubble from within, the bigger your bubble gets. Therefore, you can roam around within your bubble and venture into what's uncomfortable and outside your comfort zone with a level of comfort as your bubble expands, and you get closer to your goal with less frustration (see Figure 14).

I prefer to think of my comfort zone as a malleable bubble that expands due to my daily efforts of pushing and stretching myself. Therefore, when it comes to wanting something outside my bubble, I can choose to expand my bubble from within to get further towards what I desire. This makes my goal feel not so far away, as I've already expanded my comfort bubble so that it's nearer to my goal.

Let's put this into a real-life scenario, for example, quitting smoking. Let's say you've been a smoker for many years. Quitting would be a major step outside of your comfort zone. You're likely to step back into that comfort zone when things get too hard. Whereas if you were to add in daily exercise and a healthy meal as a regular habit and not simply focus on stopping smoking, that would be an example of stretching that comfort bubble from the inside.

COMFORT BUBBLE...

Figure 14: Comfort Bubble Diagram

You're not letting go of the behaviour at first but rather adding another technically uncomfortable behaviour. You're still keeping that other comfort for now until your bubble gets big enough where you feel so good about yourself that the new habit overtakes the older habit. You're able to let go easily and reach your target because you've stretched yourself from the inside out, *not* the outside in.

For another example, let's say you haven't exercised for years. If your friends who regularly exercise want you to come on a five-mile run with them or to climb a mountain as a group, there's no way you could keep up. This would be a perfect example of leaping out of your comfort zone. However, maybe you could run or walk to the end of the street for three to five minutes. You increase that to five to seven minutes the next day, seven to ten minutes the day after that, 11 to 12 twelve minutes, then 15 minutes and so on. Within a few weeks, you may be able to run or walk up to 25-30 minutes without stopping. This is an example of you expanding your bubble from within to a point where you're able to roam more freely within comfort while still stretching and growing yourself.

Returning to the quitting smoking example, how about making it a rule that you must take a walk if you had to have a cigarette? In other words, you're actively keeping the comfort of the tobacco but stretching your bubble by turning smoking time into exercise time. Sooner or later, you'll start to notice one has to go.

Do you hate vegetables? If eating them as a side on your plate is too much to start, why not blend them into the food you're currently eating? Or you could turn them into soup. You could disguise them by covering them with some sauce or even hiding underneath the foods you genuinely enjoy. I remember Jamie Oliver saying when trying to get kids to eat more vegetables, "Why not add some peppers to a pizza?" Remember, you're an adult now, and adults eat vegetables. You can do certain things or add in certain behaviours while not immediately stopping the things you love or that keep you sane. Consider what you *can* do, with where you are and what you've got, that allows you to stretch your comfort bubble.

SUMMARY

Remember the bubble analogy when approaching the uncomfortable things that perhaps scare you or make you apprehensive. You don't have to leap out of your comfort zone at every chance to make lifelong changes. You can stretch or expand yourself within your current bubble without stopping or letting go of your troubled behaviour straight away.

Trying something potentially exciting and challenging while doing what keeps you certain and safe could be another way to regain self-control. You could stop those bad habits that have been holding you back for so long. By doing something mildly challenging consistently, your life shifts in small degrees. There's nothing huge to potentially terrify you and get you to quit when it gets hard. You need small, consistent changes that will lead to big long-term changes.

This gives you a chance to fall in love with the process, makes it easier on yourself and not give in when it sucks. You'll not get disheartened at the lack of results or beat yourself up because your expectations change as you become more realistic in your mindset.

I'd like you to consider the following before I move on.

Happiness equals a temporary state where you create a feeling of contentment. It's easy to choose happiness with a meal you love, a movie you adore, a night 'on the drink,' or a quick purchase to make you feel better. But when it's gone, you're often in this constant fleeting search for further happiness.

I remember someone telling me, "I stopped looking for happiness years ago because it made me so damn sad." All too often, people are chasing happiness. They look to quick fixes to give them temporary happiness. They then get deluded when they have to get uncomfortable and wait for results, so they switch from one quick fix to the next.

Please consider this different approach.

Fulfilment equals an ongoing, genuine love of the process. This is where you fall in love with the process, no matter what it brings. You love it even during the low times, the times you mess up, the unmotivated times, the sad times, the ups and the downs, the positives and the negatives. You can either choose to love it or choose to suffer. These are your only two options.

This way of thinking is super effective if you maintain the perspective that, yes, some weeks may be challenging, but you can always find some lessons or deep appreciation if you look hard enough. Problems come when you choose to be a victim of your complaining. I understand it's popular and often cathartic to complain. People resonate with you as they tend to have a lot to complain about too. Therefore, you get significance and acceptance, and those feelings are often too tempting to deny. But in reality, that's known as trying to blend in. You can't stand out and blend in at the same time. You weren't born to blend in. You are more unique than you possibly know. We all are. I truly believe in this perspective of not being so fixated on chasing happiness and expecting it to be precisely the way you want it to be because it's so frequently disappointing.

A much more helpful approach is to start engineering your fulfilment by understanding how you can be happier and more in love with the process. This will help you escape a tonne of heartache and disappointment and help you appreciate the whole magnificent journey of this beautiful thing called *your life*. Now, let's look at getting a handle on your day-to-day energy and learn how to ramp it up naturally.

CHAPTER 5

HOW TO SUPERCHARGE YOUR NATURAL ENERGY

Earlier in Chapter 1, I asked you to audit several areas of your life. Firstly, I asked you to rate your energy out of ten, with ten being the most or best and one being the least or worst. Supercharging your energy is when your energy reaches eight, nine, or ten out of ten.

Making useful and clear decisions that positively impact you is harder to do the less energised you feel in your life. Everything is more challenging when you're tired. Your food choices suck. You're a 'ratty dick' to your partner. You're shouting and snapping at the kids. Little things that wouldn't usually bother you grind on you or cause you to overthink. It's astonishing how much worse we all handle our emotions when we're tired. And yet some of us just stay tired all week, every week, and think that that's just the way it's supposed to be. We're too tired to go to the gym, cook decent food, read a book or go on a date night.

I remember back when I used to party almost every weekend. The typical routine was countless amounts of vodka, lime and soda, often a bag of the white powder (cocaine), followed by a few puffs of weed (cannabis) to get to sleep, and a garbage diet the entire day after.

Over the next few days, I'd be down in the dumps, low, miserable and completely 'knackered'. It'd take till Tuesday or even Wednesday to feel normal again. It's unbelievable how our choices at weekends can ruin our good feelings. Even if you don't drink or do drugs, the break from the routine of your bedtimes and what you do or don't eat can play havoc on your feelings for several days afterwards.

I understand that it's the norm for most people to let their hair down at the weekend. But, by now, perhaps you've realised that those choices are not letting you live the way you want to live. Many people are living their lives as walking zombies. I'm here to tell you if your energy is 'off,' your life is going to suffer. You need to work on changing this. So, strap yourself in, my friend, because this is where I come alive!

You may have already developed enough energy to get through your workday with no problems. You've become, as an old mentor of mine used to say, 'work fit,' where you can do your job no matter what. But over time, your enthusiasm drops, and you find yourself having less and less energy, before or after work, to do the things you want to do.

Unfortunately, the easiest thing for most people to do when they're tired after a hard day at work is to order a takeaway and sit on their backside for several hours in front of the TV. Long term, that behaviour will only stimulate you so far before you become more bored, worn out, and have a lack of drive to do anything new or challenging.

Your energy levels are in direct correlation with your happiness and fulfilment levels. I'll state this firmly. You can't be fully happy if you're constantly tired.

> You can't be fully happy if you're constantly tired.

You can't be the best version of yourself or produce your best work when you're lethargic and drowsy. Your energy levels must be your priority every *single* day. Why wouldn't they be? Why would you actively choose to stay tired on a day-to-day basis? High energy keeps you resilient, tough and most of all, excited. Remember, an exciting life is a happier life. So how do you not only fix your energy levels but keep them at a supercharged eight to ten level?

FOUR OVERLOOKED EMOTIONS FOR NATURAL ENERGY

I say *natural* energy because you can get temporary boosts of energy from a can of Red Bull or Monster energy drink, or you can slurp a strong coffee to get a hit. Hell, you can fill every day with those things and get by. But in the absence of these things, could you perform and produce?

Most people rely on stimulants for energy and believe that all energy is physical. While a lot of your natural energy will come from becoming fitter and healthier, there are four emotions that many people greatly overlook when it comes to becoming and staying naturally full of energy.

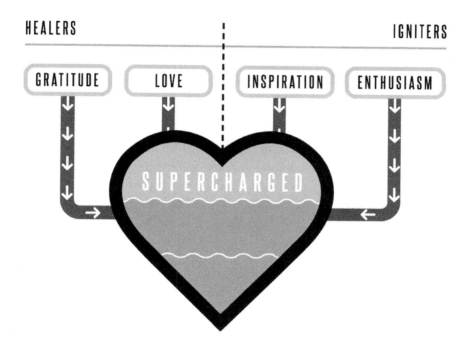

Figure 15: Wholehearted Diagram

1. GRATITUDE

You've heard people say, "Develop an attitude of gratitude." You may roll your eyes at the old cliches, but almost all the cliches you hear are usually accurate. You hear them all the time, but are you putting into practice what you hear? Most people aren't.

According to the Google dictionary, gratitude is the quality of being thankful and readiness to show appreciation for and return kindness. Just think for a second about the openness and willingness required to allow yourself to fall into that state fully. It's not easy. However, what is easy is being negative, complaining about the world, the government, and how everyone else isn't acting the way they should.

You may experience a lot of resistance to being thankful and open to positive forms of appreciation because of the painful things that happened to you in the past. Your brain is wired to look for threats to keep you alive. It's your brain's job. Therefore, it's so much easier to be negative. If it's your brain's job to keep you alive, you'll always unconsciously seek out what's wrong or bad. It's why most people will complain about things. They'll often strike up connective conversations with others about what they can relate to, which of course, is by complaining.

The power in gratitude for lifting your energy levels is immense. Just consider your posture when complaining and talking about what's wrong. It's likely to be low and hunched over. Your chin is probably down, your gaze near the floor, and your tone of voice is low. Your energy is most likely low too. It could be high, but high negative energy can be just as destructive as low negative energy, if not more.

However, when you're stating or feeling what you're grateful for, your posture is taller, your gaze may lift slightly, and you'll either look up, or your head will wobble side to side. You may also find your tone of voice becomes more optimistic and possibly higher in pitch. You'll feel you want to move around more as you talk and express gratitude. Actively expressing gratitude changes your state and energy fast. When you execute the attitude of being grateful frequently, you'll see just how your natural energy rises. You'll have more appreciation for the bad things as well as the good.

Always remember, the universe is never really against you, although it may feel like it at times when you're not frequently demonstrating being grateful. Yes, it's full of ups and downs, highs and lows, and positives and negatives. There's evidence everywhere to support this in your own life. But, if you can be grateful for the journey and appreciate the process, you'll find yourself far more energised daily. You'll find yourself searching for solutions to move forward rather than dwelling on the past and feeling run down. You'll also find yourself being kinder to others when you start expressing willingness to be kinder to yourself.

There is real, true power in becoming more grateful and appreciating what is good in your life. When you're grateful, you're more willing to return the kindness as a mirror reflection of your attitude inside. Your attitude is everything. Be more grateful.

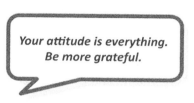

*Your attitude is everything.
Be more grateful.*

Here's a list of actions you can take to express gratitude:

- Write down three to five wins of the day before bed.
- Tell someone (in-person, call, text, etc.) two to three things about them that make you feel grateful.
- Appreciate an area of your body out loud in the mirror, even if you don't think it's perfect.
- Be grateful in advance by tipping at a restaurant before you begin your meal.

2. LOVE

Love is a funny subject. We all have something or someone we love. But in terms of keeping your energy high, there's nothing quite like self-love. This is a feeling many people have difficulty expressing wholeheartedly. The very notion of loving yourself seems to come with the idea of being selfish, when in fact, it's quite the opposite. Self-love and self-care are among the most caring acts you can undertake. Not just for yourself, but others too.

When your kids are acting up, you're tired and can't be bothered, are you more likely to be super patient with them and speak to them kindly, or are you more likely to lose it, shout and bawl, and then feel guilty about it later? What about other people around you, such as friends and family? I bet you're a pain when you're tired? Don't worry, me too.

But, what if you've done something in the day that makes you feel genuinely good and doesn't have any negative downsides or after-effects? What if you've given yourself a little bit of self-love, like a hot bath or a well-earned half-an-hour to chill with music and candles? Even a sweaty session in the gym where you only need to focus on yourself for an hour works well.

It's little acts of self-love and self-care that help you feel better about yourself inside. They help express a better version of you that's more useful to you and those closest to you.

Your family doesn't want an out of shape, unhealthy and fat dad who's unhappy with his body, drinking most nights and constantly shouting at the kids. It doesn't matter how many PlayStations and gadgets they have or how big the house is if their grumpy dad is always a miserable bastard because of his lack of self-care. Likewise, a mother who neglects herself, cooking and cleaning all day, always doing for others and feeling underappreciated, never spending time on her makeup, dressing up or feeling sexy. This will weigh heavily on her heart, not to mention feeling heavier in her clothes. This may also drive her partner to lose attraction for her, perpetuating the cycle further.

But, with a little bit of self-appreciation, you'll naturally uplift your energy. Raise your standards a little by increasing regular acts of self-love to naturally uplift your energy and your life for the benefit of everyone. The more you express these acts of kindness and love to yourself, the more you'll develop the habit of lifting yourself and growing your self-esteem.

Here are some more self-love ideas:

- Buy a new item of clothing you've wanted for ages and arrange a date night on Saturday.
- Cook a meal from scratch full of healthy goodness to nourish you and your family.
- Spend half an hour playing the guitar, using your hands with something creative you enjoy doing, or listening to the new album from your favourite band on iTunes.

- Drink loads of water throughout the day till your pee is completely clear by 5 PM, therefore looking after your hydration levels and inner health.
- Sit with a cup of tea or coffee for an hour and read a book.
- Compliment yourself for what you *have* done this week, rather than beating yourself up for what you haven't done.

3. INSPIRATION

You can be hit by external inspiration at any time. You can be inspired by seeing a guy in a wheelchair smiling in the supermarket. You can feel inspired by watching a 90-year-old guy lifting weights on Instagram. You can get a burst of inspiration from seeing a friend overcome a bad patch and pick themselves up and carry on, reminding you to stop with your 'pity party.' The problem is that inspiration, like motivation, comes and goes. How do you stay constantly inspired?

According to the Google dictionary, inspiration is the process of being mentally stimulated to do or feel something, especially to do something creative. Inspiration is such an effective tool for creating natural energy, yet it's often overlooked in our lives. Most people don't spend enough time pursuing inspiration and spend too much time indulging in drama. You can't just wait for inspiration to hit. You need to seek it out actively.

Look again at the definition of inspiration. Notice the last part, "especially to do something creative." When you're creating, you're usually at your best. You require far less motivation when you're in that kind of creative flow.

These days, people consume far more than they create. They're scrolling through social media, watching too much YouTube and TV, and indulging in other people's content. They also distract themselves from creative inspiration by drinking, eating and partying too much. This further reduces their capacity to concentrate and indulge in inspiring activities because they're drained of energy.

When you're taking action, perhaps trying new things, and feel like you're making progress, you'll experience lasting inspiration from within you. You'll feel compelled and pulled towards something.

You need to nurture this feeling of inspiration daily. When you decide to create memories and opportunities in your life, it's a surefire way to further happiness and inspiration. You can break the word inspiration down further to mean 'in spirit.' Even though you're initially externally stimulated, something inside you causes you to be 'in spirit' and act. When you act from a place of being inspired internally, you're 'in spirit' and creatively acting from within.

Whether you can achieve constant inspiration depends on what you regularly listen to, watch and do. Stop watching the news or reading the newspapers, if you haven't already. Those things do nothing but disempower you and make you feel negative. Expose yourself to external inspiration by following inspiring people online, listening to inspiring podcasts, reading inspiring books, watching inspiring documentaries or YouTube videos, and spending time with people ahead of you in this game of life. Nurture your internal inspiration by indulging in creative activities, such as drawing, building, painting, colouring, etc. These are just a few examples of creative work that trigger constant inspiration.

Actively inviting inspiration externally and creating inspiration internally will inspire you to achieve your potential. You'll lose the need for motivation to achieve the things you want if you're truly and constantly inspired. If you need motivation, you're not inspired enough, and you'll feel the need to push yourself to do things. Motivation pushes. Inspiration pulls.

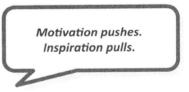

Motivation pushes. Inspiration pulls.

Here's a list of actions to regularly inspire you:

- Listen to motivational speeches on YouTube (or my 'Supercharged' videos).
- Colour in or draw.
- Read a fiction book, a graphic novel or a comic book.
- Visit a museum or art gallery.
- Walk without your phone, in nature, for 20-30 minutes.

- Stop watching the news or reading the newspaper.
- Listen to a new podcast.
- Watch a documentary instead of a TV show or film.

4. ENTHUSIASM

Enthusiasm is having more energy and excitement for a particular thing. According to the Google dictionary, the definition of enthusiasm is intense and eager enjoyment, interest or approval. I love that! Intense and eager enjoyment is key. Imagine for a second if you were intensely eager more often in life.

You may have bursts of enthusiasm, such as when the new Marvel movie comes out or when two famous boxers have their first-ever encounter. Perhaps you feel eager when you're boarding the plane for the holiday of a lifetime. Or when it's Christmas Eve and you're living vicariously through your children's excitement. You could be eager when you're about to 'get laid' in a hotel, and you know she's in the bathroom getting into her best lingerie.

We all have periods in our life when we're enthusiastic and passionate. But maintaining these periods is difficult. This is why you must plan and prioritise regular activities that make you eager. Activities that are fun and not done out of a feeling of duty. Activities that you're genuinely enthusiastic about, but you never think you should do or must do. You *want* to do them. You *want* to get laid more. You *want* to play video games. You *want* to get a great body. You *want* to play more guitar. You *want* to spend time on your own or with friends. You *want* to walk more, etc.

A little planning and being strict about scheduling these events goes a long way. Why wait six months until your summer holidays or Christmas to get enthusiastic about having some time off? I know there are things in your life that you'd love to do now, or you used to love doing as a teenager, that you've let slip because life got in the way. Do you think you're too old to enjoy those things now?

Look at me, for example. I'm a 36-year-old adult male who still watches the WWE Attitude Era from 1999, plays retro video games on N64 and PS2, and listens to Iron Maiden from 1988. I still enjoy what I enjoyed as a teenager. You probably still enjoy those kinds of things too. Love what you love, and don't be afraid to schedule those enthusiastic activities of yours frequently. There's a big kid in you somewhere!

Here are some ideas to generate daily enthusiasm:

- Move your body more.
- Dance!
- Bounce on a trampoline.
- Pre-order the thing you've wanted for a while.
- Tell people your goals and why you want to go for them.
- Spend time with an enthusiastic peer group.
- Unfollow anything or anyone on social media that drains you.
- Plan your week on paper.
- Entertain yourself by doing or watching something that used to excite you as a teenager. A little nostalgia could do it for you. It works wonders for me.
- An extra tip. Always try to share your enthusiasm. It's infectious!

DOING THINGS WHOLEHEARTEDLY

When you think about having a great life, I'm sure you agree that it involves feeling an abundance of the four overlooked emotions (gratitude, love, inspiration and enthusiasm). Whatever you choose to achieve in your life, when you have these four feelings in abundance, you're likely to feel wholehearted and understanding of the process. However, when you feel your life is just a dull, mundane existence, your approach to things will be half-hearted at best. This is because these four emotions aren't flowing within you.

You know when your life feels great, as you'll feel these positive emotions flow more frequently and intensely throughout your day. As you saw in Figure 15 (Wholehearted Diagram) at the beginning of this chapter, once you fill your heart with these four emotions for natural energy, you'll feel a sense of healing. You may even gain the ability to let go of things in the past that hurt or deeply burdened you. You'll also feel a fire ignite in your belly, creating motivation, courage and confidence to get things done. The more you allow these four emotions to flow through your heart fully, the more you'll achieve.

LETTING GO OF GUILT AND SHAME

Guilt and shame are two of the most debilitating and crippling emotions you can experience and hold onto for a long time. They drag you back and pull you down, and your unwillingness to let go of them could be your downfall. You may have let someone down, perhaps more than once, or you may have neglected to spend time with the kids in exchange for making more money. You may have gotten yourself into debt. You may have been short-tempered with your partner or have a string of broken promises or perceived failures.

I'd like you to consider for a moment, without judging your past, that gratitude and love are two of the most underutilised and most potent *healers* for you moving forward. If you're focused on how wrong you were or how that shouldn't have happened, you're going to get more of that coming your way in some form.

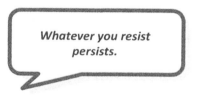

Whatever you resist persists.

If you're holding onto some resentment or anger towards yourself or someone else, I can guarantee you're not expressing love or gratitude in your life. Whatever you resist persists.

Gratitude is being appreciative for what you already have, and that includes finding some solace in your disappointments. Constantly beating yourself up benefits no one. Finding some kind of love for what is and what was will be the foundation of you moving forward. Remember, everything happens *for* you, not *to* you. It's your job to see this. Understanding this will help fill your heart and give you a naturally rejuvenated spirit. It's not easy, but it's a worthwhile road to travel down.

Love is neutral. In its purest form, it's unconditional. It embraces both the positive and the negative, the ups and the downs. It truly is an acceptance, not a resistance, to what is and will be. Surrendering to this fact is often the hardest thing to do. Self-care plays a major role in filling your heart via acts of self-love and contributes towards healing your heart. As I've discussed, you must *make* time for it and do what works for you, without the negative side or after effects, like a hangover or feeling guilty about a behaviour. You never regret the positive actions you take.

IGNITING YOUR HEART

Once you've done enough healing, there will come a time when you're ready to feel reignited and step up to the next challenge or next level in your life. Inspiration and enthusiasm are the key ingredients to fire up your life. To become more inspired and enthusiastic, you've got to start creating more excitement in your life. I say creating because excitement is created from within you. It's not given to you. You can't take a pill and be genuinely excited. Yes, I can understand the initial excitement of the intense feelings an ecstasy pill can give you. But it's not useful for a healthy lifestyle and great brain function.

Excitement is an emotion that will keep you going, give you that little fire in the belly and have you looking forward instead of dwelling on the past. Every morning, I say to myself and my clients, "Give me one thing to be excited about today." I've said this before, but I need to repeat it here. If you haven't created anything to look forward to, you'll unconsciously create things that you don't look forward to and don't excite you. It doesn't have to be anything big. It could be something simple to start. Appreciate the small wins so that you can fully appreciate the big wins in all their glory when they come. It's your duty to schedule excitement into every single day.

Once you choose excitement and make sure to get it every day, you're going to be more motivated. Imagine your life with a higher frequency and intensity of excitement. It only happens when you make it a habit.

SUMMARY

Gratitude, love, inspiration and enthusiasm are the most overlooked areas for boosting natural energy and overall happiness. Use the bullet lists I've given you in this chapter for action steps to naturally inject yourself with these powerful emotions.

Developing a deeper understanding of this wholehearted philosophy and adopting the strategies I advise will bring you vast improvements in your natural energy and mental health.

In the following chapters, you'll look into physical and emotional relationships and the world of work in more detail. I'll also provide resource links and QR codes to help you. I recommend you pay close attention to these valuable resources and use your phone to access them.

CHAPTER 6

SUPERCHARGING YOUR PHYSICAL BODY

Have you ever wondered what your body actually is? I'd like you to open your mind a little and think about the philosophy of your physical body. Your body is truly a marvellous vehicle that helps you navigate through life. Consider your mind to be the driver of that vehicle.

Is your body in good condition? The better your vehicle is fuelled and prepared, the easier and faster you'll be able to navigate this turbulent and often uneven ground you'll be venturing through as you drive your way through life.

Unless you decide to sit on your arse for all eternity, you'll undoubtedly hit some bumps in the road. You'll meet some setbacks and some serious challenges in your quest to progress in life. It makes sense to have your vehicle (body) in tiptop physical shape so that these bumps are easier to deal with and you can plough on without having to take time out. Having a highly conditioned and in shape physical body will help alleviate the fear you experience and allow you to deal with the knockbacks more swiftly and with more ease. I know for sure that your self-confidence always increases due to a more physically in shape body.

Never doubt the power of having a more physically equipped body to deal with harsh or challenging emotions. It's like your physical armour that not only supports your internal health but your emotional wellbeing too. The stronger your body is, the more resilient it is to fear.

> *Never doubt the power of having a more physically equipped body to deal with harsh or challenging emotions.*

Fear is felt physically inside the body. It's that knot in your stomach, anxiety in your chest, or tightness in your shoulders or jaw. You can deal with stress far more easily the more physically fit and strong you are.

Please understand that I'm not saying you must have a six-pack, be ripped or be a certain weight to handle your life. What I'm saying is that it's your duty, not just for your health alone, to be in the best physical shape you can be. Not fat and wheezing while walking up the stairs or running after the kids, and not skinny, scrawny, and so weak you can't break a pencil. There needs to be some middle ground where you feel in control of your physical shape, your capacity to be useful, and do the things you want to do.

Here are a few eye-opening facts. Your body is made up of hundreds of trillions of cells, all working to keep you alive every second. More than half of your body weight is made up of water, and your bones are pound for pound stronger than steel. A block of your bone could support up to 18,000lb (over 8000kg) of weight. Your brain also contains about a hundred billion nerve cells. It's incredible what our bodies are, what they contain and what they're capable of doing.

It's almost incomprehensible talking about these mega numbers. But one thing you can wrap your head around is the idea that you need to be more loving and appreciative of your vehicle, which guides you through life. Your body is a gift, and you only get one. It's time to look after it and treat it like you would that £100,000 Ferrari you'd display proudly on your drive and take pictures to post on social media. You'd absolutely not let it get old and rusty. Why not treat your body the same way? Why not have a body that makes you proud?

SEDENTARY LIVES ARE RUINING OUR PHYSICAL HEALTH

According to Forbes, sedentary (sit-down) jobs have increased approximately 83% since 1950.[6] Just think about that for a second. We all have become less active in our lives due to modern technology. Before computers, almost every job was active. People were on their feet all day, moving their limbs and working their muscles through manual labour.

Decades ago, obesity was a rich man's disease. Only those with vast wealth could afford to sit around all day and have copious amounts of food. It was usually kings, queens or people in high power and influence that could afford to be fat and lazy. Everyone else needed to be active through the years, therefore burning a tonne more calories than people do now through constant movement. Food, of course, was rationed, and people only ate what they needed.

Nowadays, you can sit on your arse all day and stuff your face for very little money. Food is cheaper, and longer hours in sedentary jobs have taken over. Having been a full-time plumber earlier in my life, I know the toll a manual job can take on the knees and back over time if you're not well equipped with suitable PPE (Personal Protective Equipment) and recovery strategies. However, the biggest problems nowadays come from *lack* of movement, rather than being on your feet all day.

Sitting on your backside in front of a desk is terrible for your hips, back and knees. No matter how expensive your leather, high back, massaging ortho-paedic chair is, there is no substitute for movement of your body for helping those aches and pains. Even surgeons and sports therapists will encourage movement shortly after surgery or an injury to promote blood flow and increase muscular resistance to aid strength and overall recovery.

If you're tight in and around your body, you'll know how uncomfortable that feels and how much you can be prone to injury. Without movement, there's more likelihood of blood clots and muscle spasms, and even muscle tears from being tight and immobile. Not only that, you're more likely to be in ill health because of the lack of healthy blood flow around your body, which normally aids your organs and internal bodily systems. The more active you are, the healthier you are on the inside. In reality, there is no excuse these days for not moving. Even if you have a sit-down job, you can still get your step count up.

Stand up every hour. Use a timer on your phone or set your Fitbit or smartwatch to buzz every hour to remind you to walk. Use your phone as a pedometer to track your steps. Try going up and down the stairs, walking to lunch or just around the office. Aim for 10,000 steps a day as an ideal target to ensure you have enough physical activity. It's quite a challenge at first. If you're new to counting steps, start with 5,000 per day in your first week and then 7,500 the following week. Build up to 10,000 per day.

After that, keep 10,000 steps a day as your base minimum for a generally active lifestyle. Always remember. Your movement is your medicine, and your health is your wealth.

> *Your movement is your medicine, and your health is your wealth.*

SIX SIMPLE WAYS TO START GETTING MORE PHYSICAL

Exercise doesn't always have to be about running, lifting weights or doing pushups, although these are fantastic and more challenging ways to keep you fit and strong.

Consider that it's not always important *what* you do but *how* you do it. Yes, there will always be some idiot saying, "You should do this or that," because they love it, without even asking you what you'd love to do or try. Many people like imposing their opinion on others. But, just because someone else is passionate or enthusiastic about their chosen exercise doesn't mean it's necessarily right for you.

1. GET YOUR 'NEAT' UP

NEAT stands for Non-Exercise Activity Thermogenesis, a sexy term for calories burned via movement outside of structured exercise, such as gym work or running. Of course, you burn calories when you push your body through exercise. But, outside of this, you may be surprised that your body burns calories doing nothing, even when sleeping. The more you move outside of exercise, the more your NEAT rises. This means you burn more calories without touching a dumbbell or even putting on your trainers.

Because most people are sitting down for most of the day, their NEAT gets neglected, even though they're hitting a strenuous 30-60 minutes daily exercise session. If you're sitting all day after working out, you're missing an opportunity to burn even more calories from general movement. This means that, while the gym is great, you could expend just as much and perhaps more calories and energise yourself by simply moving about a lot. Not only that, general movement is free and simple to do.

Examples of NEAT are:

- dancing to 90s trance (or chosen favourite music) in the kitchen while cooking
- taking the stairs and not lifts
- walking around the car park at lunchtime
- intense housework
- polishing the car
- doing the gardening
- helping someone move house
- going up and down your stairs at home more often
- parking further away from the supermarket, so you have to walk further
- watching less Netflix and TV and going for a walk outside instead

All of these simple things add up. It's not always about doing what others do or what you've been told. You may be aware of the phrase, "You can't out-train a bad diet." Well, likewise, it's very difficult to 'out-exercise' a sedentary lifestyle. The most important thing is that you simply move.

> *"You can't out-train a bad diet." Well, likewise, it's very difficult to 'out-exercise' a sedentary lifestyle.*

Other examples of exercise that don't involve the typical gym or running could be:

- rock climbing
- trampolining
- dance lessons
- swimming
- rowing
- ice skating
- roller derby
- football, rugby or other ball sports

There are a tonne more ways to exercise, move, feel good, burn calories and get your NEAT up. Just remember, you should always be doing what *you* love to do, that challenges you and that you can keep up consistently every day.

I remember the great strength coach, Dan John, saying, "If it's important, do it every day. If it's not important, don't do it at all." What a great bit of advice!

2. WALKING

I purposely left out my favourite exercise in the previous list because it's the most overlooked and deserved a dedicated paragraph or two. Did you know walking before meals can help regulate digestion, so you better digest and tolerate your food? Were you aware that walking is one of the lowest impact exercises for the knees and hips and one of the easiest forms of exercise to start?

No matter how old you are, walking is one of the most efficient forms of exercise and movement for mental health, clearing the conscience and feeling refreshed. You can listen to a podcast, make a work call or socialise with friends while walking. You can hold hands with your partner and get quality time, even have deep and much-needed, distraction-free conversations, something most other forms of exercise won't permit or make easy. You can choose a different view every day. You can walk at any time of day and be free to choose your route. Walking is one of the most magnificent forms of exercise, yet most people don't make time for it. You should always make time for a daily walk, even if you only have ten minutes.

3. FLEXIBILITY

Flexibility is an issue for most men and some women. Most people spend their lives either standing up, sitting on a chair or lying down flat. Their stretching routines, if they have any at all, usually consist of pushing against a wall with their foot flat, stretching out calves before a run, or lifting their foot to touch their butt thinking they're giving their quads a great stretch. That's about the extent of most people's stretching routine.

I need to bring to your attention the importance of being flexible, regardless of whether you're a male or female. Flexibility does not just help prevent injury from tightness, but it also aids healthy blood flow around the body. This allows you to touch your toes, tie your shoes and get around in day-to-day life without puffing and panting.

4. FOAM ROLLER

You could help yourself enormously by investing in a foam roller for your legs and back. I'd recommend starting with a soft foam roller before moving to a hard plastic version with external rubber. Believe me. At first, it's uncomfortable to the point of excruciating pain. You'll want to avoid it the first few times as you'll think it's making you worse. However, just like your first sports massage (also very valuable, and I highly recommend regular sessions), the more you do it, the more familiar you'll become and the easier you'll cope with the pain. The benefit of lengthened and less sensitive muscle fibres will be valuable to you and your training.

I foam roll my quads, glutes and back for about three to five minutes, two to three days a week, before my weightlifting sessions and alongside other mobility drills. It helps prime my muscles to take on load and feel more ready for the breakdown of intense physical exercise.

5. MASSAGE

You could try self-massage with a foam roller, as I explained previously, or you can opt for tennis balls or massage balls that you lay on areas of your body to stimulate your muscles and relieve tension. Many people have found them to be useful.

However, I prefer a specialist hands-on approach. I have a sports massage guy who I see about once every three to four weeks. He works out any niggles or knots in my back and legs, which is necessary to help me stay consistent in my active lifestyle (if you want his details, please check the Resources section at the back of this book). I suggest you also don't avoid regular massages. They can help you keep on top of things. When could you book in for your next session, or perhaps your first one?

6. YOGA

Writing about yoga is a fascinating subject. The very idea of yoga makes most men run a mile! Skinny, hot women in leotards or overly happy, lean vegan men with ponytails and beards who are so calm it scares the hell out of you. This is most people's perception of yoga teachers.

It's a standardised and generic stereotype, and, to be fair, I've met quite a few people who fit the bill. But here's something for you to consider. Those who regularly practice yoga are usually in great shape, and they're always, to some extent, very *happy* in their energy. There's something to learn from this, just like I did when I spent three days living with Zen Buddhist monks. Those guys are happy!

I was first introduced to yoga after hearing my local town had a hot yoga class. This is where you perform yoga in a heated room. The heat helps your muscles stretch further and enables you to detox more through sweating. Being quite an open-minded, up-for-anything kind of guy, I loved the idea of sweating in a new environment and having a new challenge. However, I didn't like the idea of being in a class full of people better than me. I didn't want to be surrounded by smoking hot women or men with single figure body fat composition doing handstands. In the meantime, I'm falling over, trying to wrap my leg around my head and looking like a complete idiot!

I was vastly mistaken. The class was full of average people. A few were overweight. I wondered how often people had put themselves off doing yoga by making up stories just like I did. The teacher took us through what they call a flow, where you move your body slowly through tight areas, opening up your body in ways it has never opened before. Flow allows you to breathe slowly and slow down your mind to aid your body into the various positions. I found I was pretty tight in areas I didn't even know I had areas.

Thankfully, I'm reasonably flexible compared to most guys because of the positions I hit in my other training sessions, such as low squats, high pulls/pushes, etc. But yoga was a new environment for me, challenging me in a completely different way. What I realised was the most challenging part is judging your early efforts. If you ever do any new exercise or training, you'll know this is true. It's too easy to think, "Holy shit, I'm crap at this! I can't do this. I'm bloody useless!" All the while hating every second of your new form of exercise. Remember Zig Ziglar's quote. Your attitude determines your altitude.

Yoga exposes you. It reveals where you're tight, unfocused, unbalanced, where you can't switch off, and where you feel pain. For most men, their ego just won't let them switch off from that constant judging of their early efforts, which is self-abuse. They've become so good at beating themselves up through their consistent judgement of their early efforts that they always talk themselves out of things without ever really giving themselves a chance to get better.

My partner and I attend yoga together once a week at Hotpod Yoga in Whitley Bay, where we do an hour's yoga flow with one of their brilliant instructors. I also hire a yoga coach to take my TST members through a great flow once a month. Additionally, I have a Tuesday replay ritual for our online guys to help them keep up their weekly practice. I'm no yoga expert, but I use yoga weekly to aid my physical recovery. Not only that, since I've learned to stop judging my early efforts so harshly, I've found yoga enormously beneficial for my mental health, levels of calm and general focus. I've noticed how better I handle my stress when a regular yoga practice is in place. Most of my clients, many of whom are tough, 'manly' men, enjoy the great benefits yoga can bring to their lives and how it can be a great addition to their overall strength, core stability and flexibility. They feel less tight, less stiff and younger as a result.

Listen to me carefully here. Yoga has done wonders for my sex life. Being more flexible has enabled me to get into deeper positions that have helped immensely with the intimacy and pleasure of intercourse. If you're still sceptical, I cannot recommend the documentary Relentless on Amazon Prime more highly. It features DDP (Diamond Dallas Page), the former professional wrestler who broke his back and found yoga. It's an emotional ride and a real eye-opener for anyone sceptical about yoga.

RESISTANCE WORK

Earlier in this chapter, I listed examples of exercise that didn't involve the typical gym or running. While these are all great, millions of people already do or would thrive in a gym style environment. Doing resistance work, i.e., lifting weights or working with your body weight, is one of the best ways of getting in shape and feeling great in the process.

I attribute most of my physical figure and success in health and fitness to a combination of lifting weights and bodyweight training, four to six days a week. Never overlook resistance work. Getting fitter and stronger physically not only helps your body change shape and look more aesthetically appealing, but it also strengthens your bones, aids in posture, and reduces your chances of further physical ailments as you age. You've all seen the videos of granddads lifting weights in their late 70s and 80s online. You've seen the 66-year-old grandma blasting out full pushups on Tiktok. You should never stubbornly turn your nose up at getting stronger.

I've coached thousands of people over the years and studied with some of the absolute best in the field of health and fitness. When it comes to weights and weightlifting, it's bewildering how many people I see only following what they see in their gym or on their online feed. For example, Monday is chest day, Wednesday is back and shoulders day, Friday is leg day, and Saturday is arms day. If this is you, have you ever stopped to consider why you decided to train like that? Why are you training body parts? You probably do it because you see bodybuilders online or in magazines and think that's what you need to do to build muscles. That was me 20 years ago.

Back in 2002, before the internet became the norm, we used to go to newsagents and buy bodybuilding magazines, such as Flex and Muscle and Fitness, and be amazed at the physiques inside the magazines. I used to read, with my mates, about the workouts of those ripped and chiselled guys like Jay Cutler, Ronnie Coleman and, of course, the greatest of all time, Arnold Schwarzenegger.

We used to look at all the supposedly *amazing* supplements and spend hundreds of pounds a month on BCAAs (Branched Chain Amino Acids) and pre-workouts, NO (nitric oxide) pumps and whey protein, only to find most of the supplements we'd bought were peed out and left our wallets significantly lighter by the end of the month.

A quick note on supplements. Don't buy into the hype. The marketing is impressive, and I give full credit to those who write the sales copy and produce the advertising. It's compelling. But what you probably don't realise is that 95% of the people you see in magazines are on steroids. If you choose to take steroids, I need to warn you about several health consequences later in life. These include heart failure, liver dysfunction, and many joint issues. I also can't *not* mention the horrific mental side effects of going from an absolute beast while you're on steroids back to an average man (or woman) shortly after coming off them.

These people in magazines or on your Instagram feed who look out of this world are nine times out of ten on gear (steroids). And yes, even your favourite Hollywood actors that have muscles for days are likely to be on them too. It's just an unfortunate truth. I'm two decades into the gym game, and I've seen a lot. This next year marks my 20th year since I first picked up a set of dumbbells and scoffed at a scoop of whey protein. I have some time in the field. Let my experience help you out in the long term.

THE ONLY SUPPLEMENTS YOU NEED
Which supplements are worth it, in my opinion? They are:

- grass-fed whey protein or a good tasting vegan protein powder
- creatine monohydrate powder
- good quality greens powder
- good quality fish oil tablet or liquid with antioxidant protection (usually labelled as 'vitamin E')

That's really about it. Don't buy into the hype of all the garbage that's available. Unless, of course, you have a tailored supplement stack coming directly from your health care professional and *not* from your steroid abusing uncle, the jacked guy in the gym, or bodybuilding.com.

FIVE OF THE BEST PHYSICAL MOVES YOU CAN DO

I could probably write a decent-sized book on technique and strategy when it comes to training. However, as I want you to adopt something that will help you as you get older, so you suffer fewer injuries and enjoy consistent health benefits, I'll keep the approach as simple as possible.

This is something I'd never really considered in my 20s, mainly because it was all about the big chest and arms back then. If I could turn back time, I'd start with what I'm about to explain to you. You need to step away from the typical bodybuilding approach that most people follow unless you genuinely want to be a bodybuilder. I'd like to open your eyes to a different perspective.

"Train movements, not body parts." This philosophy was taught to me by Dan John, a strength coach from the USA, who blew my mind when he explained this concept. I highly recommend his teachings (please find his books in my Recommended Reading List at the back of the book). He explains five key movement patterns that you must train and prioritise to have a thoroughly efficient and strong, athletic body, no matter your age.

Those five movements are:

- squat
- push
- pull
- hinge
- carry

1. SQUAT (THE KING OF ALL MOVEMENTS)

This movement comprises maximal knee bend and maximal hip bend. This is where you sit your backside between your hips as low as you can, keep your feet flat, your knees straight or forward (not caved in) and your chest as tall as possible. You sit down like you're sitting on a chair and stand back up again. If you can't sit all the way down and your hamstrings can't touch your calves, then you could have tight ankles due to lots of sedentary work. Raising your heel may help you. You could put something under your heels to press against the floor as you squat. Or you could hold onto something to lean back further as you squat, which could help you get a better depth.

Always start with just your body weight. You could then build up to a dumbbell or kettlebell, and then potentially a full back squat and front squat with an Olympic bar. I believe the squat is the king of all exercises. As long as you add resistance, you work all your muscles because of the muscle recruitment required in a full squat. It's one of the most challenging and effective moves you could do, and you should prioritise it in your training to get stronger and more flexible. It will work your back, legs, core, grip and mental capacity.

2. PUSH OR PRESS (THE EGO MOVEMENT)

This movement is where you're pushing or pressing something away from you. Examples are a bench press, dumbbell press, shoulder press, tricep press or even dips. This is a movement most men do every Monday at the gym. I call it the ego movement because it's the one most men prioritise over other movements to their detriment. They want to brag about how much weight they can bench.

Here's the truth. Your bench shouldn't be stronger than your squat. I admit mine was back in my 20s. As I hit my 30s, I started squatting more, prioritising the more diverse movements, and benching less. Too much benching heavy over the years will lead to a rounded posture, hunched shoulders and potential shoulder injuries later down the line if you neglect the other more powerful movements. However, it's a very functional movement and should get some attention.

3. PULL (THE MOST OVERLOOKED MOVEMENT)

This movement is more important than a push or press and should get more attention. However, many people neglect this exercise because people only like to train what they see in the mirror. The back (or your posterior chain) often gets overlooked. A strong back and strong pull will aid and strengthen your push and press.

A great way to get better at benching is to row (pulling weight towards your body). Likewise, a great way to increase shoulder or overhead press is to add chin-ups or pull-ups to your routine. Your posterior chain guides you through your life. It's your main support. Therefore the muscles around your spine need attention. Your grip also needs attention. Anything you pull will challenge your grip. If your grip is engaged, so is your core as well as your mind, helping you to focus. A stronger back and shoulders through the use of any pull movements will help you take more weight on your shoulders, both physically and metaphorically.

4. HINGE (THE MOSTLY UNDERVALUED MOVEMENT)

The hinge movement is where your body tilts back from the hips with maximal hip bend and minimal knee bend. Think of a stiff-legged deadlift or kettlebell swing as examples. You could also put regular deadlifts in this category. These hinge movements help strengthen your hamstrings, glutes, lower back and hips. When performed correctly, these can significantly help in overall strength and power as well as aid in injury prevention by strengthening often neglected muscle groups.

However, if you've ever put your lower back out bending over or deadlifting, you'll know how debilitating it can be. I mention deadlift in this list because I know some people thrive from deadlifting. But, as I've suffered a few back injuries from this movement, it's something I now leave out of most of my lifting plans. Quite simply, I feel the risk to reward ratio is too great. I add the other movements I've already mentioned to strengthen and aid my body. I avoid heavy deadlifts as the risk is too high for injury. If your lower back goes, you're completely wrecked from head to toe! Maybe you've experienced this and know what I mean? It's just not worth it, in my opinion.

5. CARRY (PROBABLY THE MOST USEFUL MOVEMENT FOR LIFE)

One of the most neglected movements that not many people prioritise is a weighted carry. You simply load up your body and walk, crawl or lunge. This simple movement is where you squeeze something tight and move a distance with it, challenging your core and grip massively, not to mention your breathing, as you try to move under the resistance. It's excellent for fitness as well as strength. Examples are farmer's walks, walking lunges with kettlebell or barbell, kettlebell waiter walks, suitcase walks, overhead carries, or even prowler pushes.

TRAIN TO FEEL BETTER NOT JUST LOOK BETTER

All other moves are just things to play with, such as ab training, twists, or specific targeted body part work. If you change your training from chest and arms day to push/pull days or from leg day to squat/hinge day, you're likely to have more fun and diversity in your training and get hooked on the performance side of things rather than the aesthetics.

This is how I like to change people's minds about how they look. Don't focus your training on just looking better. Instead, train primarily to *feel* better. You'll look better as a side effect without beating yourself up too much. Another way to say this is, "Train for sanity, not vanity."

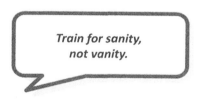

Train for sanity, not vanity.

As I explained before, there are several other ways to get fitter and stronger. There's CrossFit, park runs, team sports like five-a-side, etc. Along with regular weight training, I love bodyweight training with squats, pushups, sit-ups, planks, burpees, jumping jacks, etc., and a combination of dumbbell or kettlebell lifts, which add further resistance to the training. These activities get your heart rate up and burn a tonne of calories in a short space of time. It's what we mostly do at TST online and inside my private gym, and it's an exceptional recipe for results.

In all honesty, you have to create your own recipe for results. Think of a recipe you enjoy which includes the ingredients you love and a little of what you perhaps wouldn't do on their own, but when mixed into your recipe, the flavour just expands. Think about your training as your signature recipe that you love and could indulge in time and time again.

Within TST, we do our recipe between 6:10 AM and 7 AM in the gym and on Zoom online, where people train from their homes to supercharge their energy in the mornings. We use a mixture of bodyweight exercises with minimal equipment. Sometimes we may use the odd kettlebell or dumbbell. We structure it so it's always different, exciting, challenging and, most importantly, fun.

We do everything from a kettlebell AMRAP (As Many Rounds As Possible) to boot camp drill sergeant, body combat, animal movements, core and abs training, boxing, and everything in between. The best part is it's constantly evolving and changing depending on someone's birthday or what's happening within our group. But we'll always have a good laugh, and everyone leaves feeling like they're a part of something.

Want to know more about TST? Scan the QR code below:

FUELING YOUR BODY (WHAT YOU EAT)

You can't out-train a bad diet. You may have heard this before, and while you could eat a Mcdonald's every day, go to the gym for two hours, burn a tonne of calories and technically still lose weight, you'd feel awful. Remember, some skinny people feel terrible. The point is that you need to have a better diet.

What is a bad diet? In reality, there's no such thing as a *bad* diet. There's just diet, a word used to explain what goes into your mouth and gets swallowed. It then gets labelled good, bad, etc. You're not daft. You know that eating pizza, chips, chocolate, crisps, bread, and ice cream regularly aren't the most useful or healthy choices. A good diet fuels your body and keeps you healthy. You know that fruits, vegetables, nuts, seeds, lean meats, and natural foods are better for you.

Of course, you can technically eat what you want and still lose weight as long as your calories are in check. But that doesn't mean you're going to feel great in the process. Your body craves *nutrition* and not just calories. This is where people go severely wrong on diets. They starve themselves or restrict things like sugar, chocolate, sweets or anything else classed as bad for them. This approach usually leaves a person drained, tired and generally upset. It's no wonder many people hit the 'fuck it' switch so frequently on diets. It's also why many give up on weekends when they can't have any of their favourite things while everyone else around them indulges.

Let me help you out with some advice on balance, a word that everyone's talking about, but few seem to get right. You may be thinking, "But Luke, I'm an all-or-nothing person!" This is why you keep failing, my friend. I used to be the same. Whenever I was 'on it,' I was focused, motivated and driven. But then, if I couldn't do it all, I used to say, "Fuck it. Why bother? I'll do it later!" I'd live in the 'start on Monday' cycle of motivation, as I explained in Chapter 3.

According to the Google dictionary, balance is defined as an even distribution of weight enabling someone or something to remain upright and steady. Why do so many people have hunched postures and enlarged guts (compared to the rest of their bodies)? They spend most of their time sitting down, stressed, angry and pissed off, and then go off the rails every weekend. But their friends will say, "It's ok, it's all about balance."

Balance isn't stressing yourself out all week at work, waiting till the weekend so you can get drunk, wasting the rest of the weekend in bed, and then having the Monday morning blues all over again. Along with that behaviour, I can almost guarantee that your food choices won't help your waistline or mental energy. I'm talking about food chosen simply for convenience and initial taste to satisfy an otherwise dull day. Perhaps I'm being presumptuous, but I'm almost certain you'll agree we all choose our diets primarily for ease and convenience. Not many people want to cook and prepare food when they can just grab something quick to satisfy their hunger. I get it. When you're busy, diet goes out the window. But unfortunately, most quick choices (at work especially) aren't healthy and are filled with high calories, sugars and chemicals with very little nutritional value.

The point I raised earlier about your body craving nutrition over calories is true. Calories are units of energy that help you operate. They're present in all foods, and you need calories to function and move throughout your day. But most people have far more calories than they need. They're also not choosing nutritionally dense foods.

How do I know this? Because we're in an epidemic of fat, sick and tired people. The stats are there. You read it in the papers, see it on the news, and hear about it all the time. Obesity and ill health are on the rise. I hope to help people gain healthier and happier lives by correctly managing this thing called balance (not just in their diet but in all areas). Let's go a little deeper into what a balanced diet is.

Part of a balanced diet is eating a variety of fresh fruits and vegetables (your five-a-day). You've also heard it since you were a kid. But are you adopting that advice daily as an adult? Most people barely hit one to two portions of fruits and veg a day. I know some people who don't eat vegetables at all. They say they "don't like them."

It's time for my rant (I did warn you). Look, if you're a fully grown adult and you don't eat vegetables, you're a bloody moron. There, I said it. Yes, there may be some things like avocado or asparagus or artichoke that taste pretty strong, and their flavours aren't to your liking. But, you must find a balance of what you can tolerate vegetable or fruit wise and have some daily. Fruits and vegetables are the most highly nutritious and the lowest calorie foods (fruits have a higher calorie content). They contain compounds and naturally occurring chemicals that could prevent cancer, diabetes and other physical and mental health problems from occurring as you age. Remember, all pharmaceutical medicines come from plants. This means you must eat your fruits and veggies to stay healthy, my friend.

If you survive on energy drinks, crisps and sandwiches, don't be surprised when you quickly realise you look and feel like crap. Eating more fruits and vegetables daily could quite literally save your life. So stop being a baby, allow the aeroplane spoon, knife or fork to drive straight into your mouth and experiment with broccoli, cabbage, carrots, peas, sprouts, pak choy, spring onion, lettuce, aubergine and anything else. There are hundreds, if not thousands, of fruits and vegetables for you to try. If you don't like them cooked, try them raw, steamed, fried, baked, put into a smoothie or soup. Just eat your fruits and vegetables! Especially your veg.

IF WEIGHT LOSS IS THE GOAL

It doesn't matter how old you are, how overweight you are, how 'knackered' you feel in your body, how your hormones may be acting up or even what your grandparents said. You simply cannot outdo science. If you want to lose weight, you absolutely *must* be in a calorie deficit.

I always say to people, don't get obsessed with calories but be conscious of them. Be concerned, but don't spend your life over analysing. You'll only rob yourself of delicious things and lots of fun if you take things too seriously. Yes, you can go to the toilet and technically lose weight from dumping a giant poo. You can become dehydrated overnight and weigh less on the scales the following day after fasting for 12 hours. However, to get rid of fat in the body effectively, you must be in a calorie deficit. Let me share the following data points to help you on your weight loss journey.

WHAT IS A CALORIE DEFICIT?

Calorie deficit simply means you have fewer calories going into your body and more calories going out. Or you could say you expend more calories as energy through moving about and general bodily functions than you consume as food.

Your body burns calories even at rest. This is called metabolism. But most people far exceed their metabolism by simply eating or drinking too many calories. Your metabolism slows as you age and the more sedentary you become. Also, losing muscle mass slows your metabolism. You expend calories by moving your body day-to-day with activity and, of course, through structured exercise. The more you move, the more calories you burn.

For example, suppose you consume 2000 calories today, but you expend 2500 calories through exercise, general activity and your metabolism burning at rest. In that case, you're technically in a calorie deficit of 500 calories. Pretty simple right?

Let's say that you'd love to lose 1lb per week for the next 12 weeks. That's a target of 12lb (6.3kg) total weight loss. A 500 calorie daily deficit multiplied by seven days in a week is a 3,500 calorie deficit. It takes a 3500 calorie deficit to burn 1lb (0.45kg) of weight. Using the same logic, let's say you want to burn 2lb (0.9kg) per week. That's 24lb (10.9kg) over twelve weeks. Now, you can either consume 500 calories less per day while keeping the same activity levels or expend an extra 500 calories through further movement or exercise. This doubles your original 3,500 weekly calorie deficit to 7,000.

Which one is more appealing to you? Bear in mind both of these are challenging. The more weight you decide to lose, the harder the challenge and, very often, the more likely you are to quit if it gets too much. I suggest starting with where you feel comfortable and won't be put off by it being too difficult for you to accomplish.

In reality, all of this is simple, straightforward maths. Once you get your head around this, it's so much easier to make the shifts needed to see gradual weight loss that you can keep off. It's easier than doing a stupid diet fad that allows you to lose a tonne of weight quickly but only temporarily, ultimately meaning you can't sustain the weight loss. Worse still, months later, you could be even more fat, sick and tired than when you started.

Regarding how many calories you need specifically, you can work this out on apps like My Fitness Pal or other calorie calculators. You can download these calculators, usually for free, to your smartphone or simply search Google for them. The number of calories you need is dependent on your age, how active you are day-to-day and what kind of lifestyle you have. If you sit on your backside all day, you're going to require far fewer calories than someone who works a manual job and is on their feet all day.

Our TST 6 AM training session via Zoom and our private online community group typically burn between 400-800 calories per session. Missing just one training session can be detrimental to your weight loss progress for the week, especially if your target is the number of calories burned. How else are you going to burn those calories off? Make sure you're not skipping any of your sessions.

Keep in mind that not all calories are the same. You can become obsessed with counting calories and losing weight, as I mentioned previously. If you hate eating rice cakes, hummus and carrot sticks all day, tired as hell of the soup diet, living on low-calorie garbage, or just craving some sweet crunch, you're going to feel miserable, drained and fed up. Not just from missing eating the things you love, but also by getting hooked on calorie counting and forgetting your body thrives on *nutrition*.

Remember when you discovered the big-ass salad concept earlier? Your body needs calories for fuel to operate. There's no doubt in that. But it also needs proteins, carbohydrates, fats, vitamins and minerals. That's why it's always important to vary your food choices and invite a lot of colour into your diet through fresh fruits and vegetables.

You also have to bear in mind that all bodies are different. Many people have intolerances, allergies, or general discomfort while consuming things like dairy or gluten, but they never realise it. The only way to know if you are intolerant to something is to have a professional test. Alternatively, one of the best ways to test yourself is to have two full weeks off wheat, dairy, gluten, etc. After two weeks, reintroduce them and see what happens to your stomach, mental focus, skin, general feeling, etc. Take some time off the thing you're a little unsure of, and then judge how you react.

I've seen some people eat carbs like pasta, granola, rice and potato all day long and stay lean and strong. Granted, they are few and far between. I've also seen people have one potato and bloat out like they've swallowed a hand grenade. I've also seen others thrive on the keto approach, a diet primarily made up of good fat sources.

You have to get to know your own body and what kinds of food work best for you. A great starting point is to increase your natural protein (meat, fish or a good quality vegan protein powder) and limit your carbohydrate (rice, pasta, potato, bread and oats) until the evening or after you've exercised. I've found many people thrive on this approach. But some feel awesome after having morning oats, a shake for lunch and a salad for dinner.

Everyone is different. Your body is unique to you, and you need to try several approaches until you find the one that works for you. Try starting with the suggestions above and give yourself ten days to two weeks to decide if you need to change your approach.

A great little tool I've seen for sale is the Eatwell plate, a dinner plate with a printed design that shows you how to structure your food. You can visualise that half the plate should be vegetables, with a quarter meat/dairy and quarter carbs. Search for 'Eatwell plate' online to help you create a more healthy and balanced plate of food every mealtime.

SUMMARY

Your physical body is an incredible vehicle, helping you travel on your life's journey. Remember how important it is to look after your physical body and how much you overlook general day-to-day movement. Your normal daily activities could burn more calories than your exercise session if you choose to be more active.

Remember that:

- your movement is your medicine
- your health is your wealth

Your vehicle (body) needs the best fuel to move, and that comes from highly nutritious, calorie-conscious meals that nourish and help your body and brain thrive. Also, remember that the most significant factor determining your physical results is *consistency*.

Now, let's look into your emotional wellbeing and mental health on a deeper level to ensure the highest levels of happiness.

CHAPTER 7

SUPERCHARGING YOUR EMOTIONAL WELLBEING

This whole chapter is about helping your emotional wellbeing and mental health. There is nothing more important than you feeling good. You *must* pay close attention to how you manage your emotions and mental health as it is an 'inside job.'

Taking responsibility for your happiness is your job. Relying on and expecting someone else to make you happy is foolish and a surefire route to disappointment, misery and stress. In this chapter, you'll discover two characteristics that allow you to become a master of your own emotions, helping you stay emotionally strong and gain the tools to navigate and supercharge your emotional state and mental health. These characteristics are stability and resilience.

GETTING OVER A TRAUMATIC EXPERIENCE

When I was 14 years old, I had a bullying experience that haunted me for years. It was the year 2000, and I was with my two friends in Newcastle town centre, having our usual monthly shopping trip to spend our pocket money.

"Luke!" my two friends shouted as I walked slightly ahead of them. I looked back and could see that six to eight big lads (boys) had their attention. One of the lads used his finger to pull me towards him. I was unsure about the situation, so I told my two friends, "Howay, let's keep walking." We tried to walk away, but the group of lads quickly followed us. They gathered around me to ask where I was going. Three of them were over a foot taller than me, which meant they were at least two to three years my senior. While leaning down intimidatingly, trying to pressurise me, the biggest one said, "Give me all the money out of your pockets. Now!"

I was just 14 years old. These boys must have been 16 to 17 years old and a lot bigger than my two friends and me. I was the tallest in our group, but I wasn't confident or tough. I was terrified. I was visibly shaking, and this gang of lads could see it. They followed my friends and me into a Virgin Megastore. As I got amongst the crowd, the gang lowered their voices and whispered threats into my ear as I walked into the shop. "Get outside now," the biggest one said aggressively. I was unsure how to deal with this situation. I only had £20 as I'd just spent most of my pocket money buying a DVD. It was No Bull by AC/DC, the recording of a live gig I'd wanted for ages (I still have the DVD to this day as it reminds me of how far I've come). I remember the smaller boys in the group hanging onto the bigger boy's commands, tugging at my plastic HMV bag, which held the DVD, trying to steal it out of my hands.

I felt hopeless, scared, vulnerable and humiliated. I was ready to break down. I remember trying to keep it together as I went to the cashier at the front desk and asked, "Please, sir, would you let me stand behind the counter? I'm being threatened." As I gulped and trembled with fear, embarrassment and shame, the cashier looked at me and told me I couldn't stand behind the counter. I pleaded with him. "Please!"

The colour had drained from my face at this point. I glanced back and saw the gang of lads waiting for me to turn back around so they could carry on tearing down my confidence and ripping up my self-esteem. The cashier saw my face filled with fear and said, "If you wait there, I'll call security." I stood still as a statue as I frantically waited for security. A large man in a black jacket showed up 90 seconds later, and the gang left the shop. He took me to one side and explained, "It's ok, I'll radio the police." He also watched me walk down to the police station to explain what had happened.

I felt broken and completely shaken by this incident. I was so angry at those boys and angry at myself for not being stronger and standing up for myself. Oddly, I vividly remember the train journey home. One of my friends suggested playing Perfect Dark on the N64 when we got home (I still have that game and console). We set up the game, so it was us against the 'chavs' or 'radgies' (tracksuit and baseball-cap-wearing thugs that hung around in groups thinking they were tough). We talked about taking our frustrations out by shooting them in the video game. It worked for about ten minutes.

I've carried this burden into my adult life. This is just one of the many bullying incidents I've experienced. Perhaps you've experienced something similar? Like me, maybe your anxiety is triggered by thoughts of, "What if something like this happens again in some capacity?" I totally get the fear of feeling inadequate, not handling it, or not standing up for yourself. The problem was, as I started coming out of my teens and left comprehensive (high school), I continued to carry this rage inside. I used to punch a metal tin until my hand bled. I used to punch walls and scream. Sometimes, I used to rip my hair out.

I vented this rage through alcohol consumption when I hit 16. Thankfully, I've never been violent towards others. But I was frequently violent to myself. Then came the excessive weed smoking and ecstasy abuse at weekends, as well as sex with literally hundreds of different women. Hookers, cocaine and wild parties followed. That kind of lifestyle is not useful or fulfilling. It can tear you down and give you even more self-doubt.

If I could offer one bit of advice, it's this. The one thing that kept me sane was having a frequent *physical* routine to help my emotional wellbeing. In my teens, I discovered the gym. It was my place where I could be with me and work on my body and mind simultaneously. It was not until I got older that I realised how positive its impact was on my mental health.

MENTAL HEALTH NEEDS PHYSICAL SUPPORT

Physical training helped me understand that some people don't have an avenue to vent, so they express it in many ways, sometimes violently, often hurting others in the process. It's because they're in pain. You must understand that the world is a mirror. You act based on how you feel. You can't meet someone in pain with even more anger and resentment unless you want to add fuel to a frustrating and ego-driven argument.

I'm going to be honest here. Believe me when I say that I spent years fantasising about killing those lads who followed me into that music shop. I literally wanted them dead. If I knew how to do it or get away with it back then, I would have done it.

However, if I saw those lads now, I'd be curious about their childhood, their upbringing, and about them in general. I'd genuinely want to help them if they wanted help, of course. Over the years, as I've grown, I've realised that being consumed by rage and anger is about the most useless thing you can allow to happen to you.

What's powerful about using physical training for mental health is that it allows you to feel more compassionately about the hard times in your life. To *feel* more compassion, you must *be* compassionate to yourself. You must learn to forgive and be at peace with what was. Physical training helps you with that.

Do you want more happiness and healing in your life? Please, remember my story.

STABILITY AND RESILIENCE

STABILITY

Most people can have an emotional breakdown or feel up and down from one day to the next. And, of course, they're going to be emotionally charged when they go through grief, loss or physical pain. If they've had some kind of trauma or abuse as a child, they usually have a specific strategy for feeling low and a strategy for feeling great. Nine times out of ten, it's down to what they decide to *do* or *not* to do.

Please note. I can't say I'd be the right person to help specifically with getting over these kinds of battle scars. Before I go any further, please bear in mind that there's a possibility that you may need therapy or medication to help you and your situation. This book isn't a prescription. It's merely an alternative perspective that could be useful to you. Always seek expert advice from your trusted medical professional if you feel you need it or are unwell.

Keeping stable can be achieved by many different strategies. One strategy I've found for building further emotional stability, as explained just earlier, is having a consistent physical training routine to support your mental health. You're likely to let emotions hit you harder if you don't have this in place. Understand that fear is physical in nature. You feel it in your gut, heart and body. The more physically equipped, i.e., fit, strong and healthy you are, the more likely you will stay stable and handle your emotions more easily.

Another point to make here on stability is that nobody will ever be perfectly stable in every way. There will always be something to challenge your emotions. Certain life events will occur, whether they've happened already or will happen in the future. You must be aware that the world will show you things you don't always desire. It's up to you how you choose to show up and handle these situations.

A strong physical routine is a priority in order for you to stay stable and not lose your mind when things go wrong. Secondly, you need a more organised approach to self-assessment. This means becoming routined in discovering more about yourself, being willing to learn new things with less pessimism, and having a more open-minded, optimistic attitude. Remember, attitude is everything.

RESILIENCE

According to the Google dictionary, the definition of resilience is the ability to be happy, successful, etc., after something difficult or bad has happened. Think about that for a second. Resilience is the ability to bounce back from adversity and overcome emotionally taxing challenges.

You grow through what you go through and understand deeper.

They say you grow through what you go through, but I'd add to that and say that you grow through what you go through and understand deeper.

Understanding is the key to resilience. You become resilient when you take the time to understand *why* you failed at something. Why did that happen *for* you? Other aspects are understanding how you can do better next time, why you keep making the same mistakes, and why you don't value certain things as you believe you should. After a tough time, we all have these questions, but how often do we accept responsibility for truly discovering more about ourselves and our downfalls?

WEEKLY ACCOUNTABILITY REVIEW

Most of the time, it's easier just to pass things off because, "It's the way it's always been," or, "I was brought up this way," or, one of my favourites, "Everyone else thinks and acts the same, so it's ok." This is where you need to start auditing your progress and learning the lessons from a weekly accountability review

Every week, within my coaching programs, I ask my clients for feedback about their week. I ask them to look back over what's happened and answer a few questions to help them become more resilient when things haven't gone their way.

Here are four powerful questions you can ask yourself every week:

1.   **What were my top five wins this past week?**

This question helps you look back on the positives, no matter how small. Counting the wins helps resilience because it stacks and builds confidence that some things have been going well. It could be more time with the kids, projects that you've progressed or finished, the fact you drank more water, took more walks, enjoyed more social time, etc. Putting your mind out of what's been rubbish for a while will help you refocus on the good things you can build on further. Remember from Chapter 3. You can't build on 'shit.'

2.   **What is my mood today, out of ten, compared to earlier in the week?**

Here you'd score yourself out of ten for today, one being miserable and low, ten being energised or supercharged. Then score yourself six to seven days ago, around the same time, again out of ten. Looking back over how you may be getting better or worse can help the brain discover what's making you feel that way. What have you been doing most of this week compared to last week? Have you been more active? Have you not prioritised yourself enough this week? What's been your strategy for getting higher or lower in mood over the past couple of days? What have you been doing or *not* doing?

3. **What has been the thing or subject I've complained about most this week?**

I love this question as it always gets you thinking about your most frequent complaints. We all complain (yes, even me), but the question is, are you complaining about yourself or other people? What is specifically irritating you that you can't help but verbalise? What thing have you not got a handle on that keeps annoying you? Think this one over carefully and be honest.

4. **Remembering that my energy is the deciding factor between information and action, what are the two things I must do to protect my energy levels?**

Here, you'd find a solution and decide what action (or actions) increase your energy levels. After all, the lower your energy, the worse you handle your feelings and emotions. The higher your energy, the easier everything is. What could you prioritise that could boost your energy? More water intake? Scheduled physical exercise? Earlier bedtimes? Less screen time? You probably already know what you *should* be doing, but maybe you're not doing it. This question helps you stay more resilient and focused.

You can't build resilience unless you're willing to not only go through some crap but also understand yourself deeper. It's questions that help steer your mind. I've mentioned this before, but I'll repeat it. Your life is one truly magnificent journey of self-discovery. You'll take twists and turns on that journey, but ultimately, you're in the driver's seat.

Now let's talk about understanding yourself even further and specific strategies for wherever you tend to 'live' in your head.

EMOTIONAL HOMES

Where do you live? I'm not talking here about your home address, area or country of residence. I'm talking about the internal environment of where you live inside your head. Here you're going to look into the four rooms you have inside your head and how you can discover where you spend most of your time. You'll also learn to navigate yourself to a more serving and useful room. I like to call these rooms our Emotional Homes.

Figure 16: Emotional Homes Diagram

If you look at Figure 16, I've used the room analogy here to explain where we tend to live in our heads. After I explain what traits are inside these rooms, you'll see where you tend to reside most of the time. Although you can technically be *in between* one of the four rooms, perhaps switching from one to the other, you'll find you're spending more time in one room over the others. Let's look at where you're spending most of your time.

In the Emotional Homes diagram, you can see Past, Change, Journey and Light as rooms in your head. I'd like you to envision a hotel where the most appealing room is the penthouse at the top. The higher up the rooms you go, the better you'll see your outside world from the inside.

Start at the bottom and work your way up. Let's begin by describing what's inside each room and the traits while residing in that room. Then look at what you can do to rise beyond these rooms and get to a higher level of thoughts and emotions.

1. PAST

If you're in the Past Room, you may feel one or more of the following:

- You feel numb.
- You're sad.
- Your life feels on autopilot.
- You've lost the ability to dream.
- You feel the need to be reaffirmed in your decisions.
- You're addicted to drama, and you're frequently complaining.
- You feel like a victim.
- You always have a "yeah, but" in your spoken language.

If you reside in this room, you're focused on the past. Perhaps you're depressed or dwelling on what has been or *could* have been. You find yourself regularly feeling lost or hopeless. This is where you'd score life at one, two or three out of ten.

2. CHANGE

If you're in the Change Room, this is where you experience one or more of the following:

- You're regularly up and down.
- You're chasing the high (life is like a rollercoaster).
- You neglect yourself when you're feeling good, i.e., you stop doing what makes you feel good in the first place.
- You wear the happy mask in public, pretending everything is *ok* or *fine*.
- You know yourself at work and feel confident in your profession, but nowhere else.
- You overthink a lot.

- You're often an over analyser.
- You have frequent, anxious thoughts,
- You say "what if" a lot inside and outside your head.

Residing in this room could feel great some days. When it's good, it's good. But other days, it can be terrible and frustrating. You're constantly chasing the next high. Nothing's ever good enough. This person can open their door, leave their homes and be the life and soul of the party, or the confident one at work that everyone comes to for help. But, once their front door locks at night and they're in an environment away from work, the happy mask comes off. Yet no one would ever know they're unhappy. Maybe this is you? This is where you'd score life at around a four, five or perhaps six out of ten (on a good day).

3. JOURNEY

If you're in the Journey Room, you may feel one or more of the following:

- You're happy.
- You're motivated.
- You're excited.
- You're optimistic about change.

People in this room have momentum, feel good, even great at times, but often come to a standstill where they think they've hit a plateau or are just coasting through life. They go so far but don't realise past stories and beliefs hold them back. They're hardworking but sometimes work or play till they crash. They're the kind of people that are always on the go and don't prioritise self-care and relaxation enough. They're a hustler and hard worker and can procrastinate a lot because things are going pretty well. Here you'd score life as a seven or eight out of ten.

4. LIGHT

This is an interesting room as you may think it's the room for enlightenment or perfection. However, this room is more about flow and progress with a sense of calm and self-control. Therefore, if you do reside in the Light Room, you'd be experiencing one or more of the following:

- You're constantly prioritising progress over perfection.
- You have flow and momentum without the need for motivation.
- You're mostly calm and self-controlled.
- You do not need approval from others. You've mastered the art of self-approval and feeling complete.

This person has been on a journey and discovered a lot about themselves. You'll not find many adults under the age of 30 living in this room as it takes time to travel and navigate through life. However, small children are in this room regularly. As an adult, you may experience moments of these feelings at certain times in your life.

When someone lives in the Light Room, they accept their flaws. They have a deep appreciation of the process. They're grateful for the good, the bad, the ups and the downs. Examples of when you may experience this room might be on your wedding day, the birth of your first child, the day you finally pass that exam, etc. You experience intense feelings of elation and completion, as well as calm, flowing feelings of relaxed contentment. This is where you'd say life was a nine or ten out of ten.

Scan your Phone over the QR code below to watch a video of me explaining Emotional Homes in more detail:

WHERE ARE YOU NOW?

Once you've read through the details of each room, perhaps you can see yourself residing in one room or even a mixture of rooms. However, as previously mentioned, I'd like you to notice which room you spend the most time in and work from there. Don't choose 'special' days. For example, on your wedding day or your child's birth, you're going to be a nine or ten out of ten, obviously. On the death of a loved one, you could be two or even one out of ten. Instead, think of where you are on an average day.

We all visit every room, but what's important is that we don't stay too long in our current residence. It's vital we choose to upgrade our permanent residence, only occasionally visiting the other less appealing rooms.

You've identified which room you live in most frequently. Let's now look at how you can manage your emotions better and more skillfully navigate your way to rise to those higher feelings and emotions felt in the other rooms.

Before I move on, I must stress that most people struggle with their emotions because they try to take an express elevator from feeling an awful one, two or three out of ten in the Past Room straight up to the Light Room. This can happen with drugs, alcohol, gambling, sex, and even food to an extent. They get hooked on the immediately gratifying thing that makes them momentarily feel good in the moment. But once it's over, they get an express elevator back down and feel like crap. Cue the hangover, food coma, guilt and shame from these regretful choices.

There's no elevator to success. You must take the stairs. You've probably heard that before, but this analogy of hotel rooms in your head is proof that this statement is 100% true.

1. PAST ROOM

If you're in the Past Room, you're often looking back, stuck on what *could* have been or what *should* have been. There's a likelihood you're not taking many risks or doing much outside of your comfort zone. You'll almost certainly lack confidence, and you require a much-needed boost. You mostly feel like a victim, and you feel like nothing good happens to you.

The most effective strategy for someone feeling stuck in the Past Room is counting the wins. I call this 'stacking confidence,' or 'an attitude of gratitude.' You can perform this strategy by writing what I call 'five-to-thrive.' Every night, before your head hits the pillow, put pen to paper and write your five personal wins of the day. It doesn't have to be extravagant or extreme. It could be anything that's happened that's been remotely good. It could be that you laughed more at work, took the dog out for a walk, completed that work project, drank more water, managed the gym today or got to bed earlier. It could even be that you wrote down five wins. At the end of the day, if you can't appreciate the little things, how can you fully appreciate the big things when they eventually come?

Imagine building a wall. Each *win* is a brick you've stacked. You don't build a solid wall to protect your house in one go. You build brick by brick and stack them into a strong foundation. Five wins a day equals 35 wins in a week. Over a month, that's 140 wins a month. Over a year, it's 1,680 wins!

Consider someone that lacks confidence, always finds something to complain about, and thinks nothing good ever happens to them. Do you think having 35 things to be grateful and appreciative for every week would boost their confidence? They'd actively reflect on their past week and individual days with an expression of gratitude. As I mentioned earlier in Chapter 5, gratitude is one of the most powerful yet overlooked emotions. This is a gamechanger for anyone struggling. Yet it's so simple to do. Just make sure that a pen and paper are by your bed at night to settle your mind into a deeper, more restful sleep after recording your daily gratitudes.

If you're stuck in the Past Room and perform this exercise consistently, you'll find yourself moving to the next room.

2. CHANGE ROOM

If you're in the Change Room, you're very up and down, chasing the high and skilled at wearing the happy mask. You feel like the 'top dog' one day and then hit rock bottom the next. You're fleeting and all over the place. Overwhelm and anxiety rear their frustrating heads in this room. You can be so uncertain at times and not confident in yourself. The most compelling strategy for someone stuck in the Change Room is a morning ritual or routine.

It's astonishing how vulnerable we all are in the morning. How many times have you woken up and been instantly triggered by something someone said, what you read online or seen on the news? Maybe you've checked your inbox and immediately got that hit in the gut within minutes of waking, remembering the pressures of work or what you need to prioritise? I know that feeling all too well. It's why years ago, I understood the need to get my state and energy on point as soon as I woke up. I used many different tactics to find a morning routine that worked for me.

A little bit of advice here. Your morning routine should never involve social media, the news or checking emails. Once you put your head into that space, you're out of your body and into people-pleasing mode and the drama from other people's lives. Before you know it, you're overwhelmed, tired and don't seem to have any time for yourself. If you're watching the news, checking social media, scrolling and checking emails as you make the morning coffee, and you find yourself frequently overwhelmed, anxious and struggling with your emotions, cut it out. Now!

When your head is all over the place, it's not helpful to anyone. Your brain needs to be primed in the morning to get into a beautiful, *high-energy* and confident state. This will ensure it's more certain it can handle the day's problems.

Wake up with the focus on *you*. Remember, there is nothing more important than you feeling good. What makes you feel good? Perhaps you already know, but I'm going to give you a few suggestions that may be hugely valuable to you. Activities that put you in a beautiful state within the first 30-60 minutes of you waking up so that you can win the rest of your day. You could mix and match this list to create your own recipe that works *for* you.

Tactics that I've found work incredibly well for myself and clients I've coached are:

- breathing exercises (try the State app or the Wim Hof breathing[7] method)
- a cold shower or sea dip (one to three minutes)

- meditation (guided or silent)
- journalling
- walking
- structured exercise (like TST)
- yoga
- music that fires you up
- something that makes you laugh out loud
- conversation with a good friend
- listening to powerful motivational speeches (YouTube TED talks, videos, podcasts, etc.)
- bouncing on a trampoline

Notice how nothing here involves watching the negative news or getting involved in other people's business? I know you may think, "How can I find time for all of this, Luke?" You don't find the time. You *make* time for what's a priority. I mentioned previously about getting to bed an hour earlier. Why not wake up earlier? Stop snoozing until the last second. Give yourself 30-60 minutes every morning to prime your state and make yourself more confident. You'll find your energy levels staying higher with more self-controlled tactics.

As of writing in 2021, this is my current morning routine:

- 4:45 AM wakes me (I snooze till 5:00 AM).
- 5:00 AM Take a pee and then splash my face with cold water.
- 5:05 AM Take a pint of water with creatine, Bicarb and any supplements and boil the kettle to make V60 or Chemex coffee for Tracy and me.
- 5:10 AM Check my Stripe account and mark any money made on the money map.
- 5:12 AM Check my Whoop Band recovery (similar to Fitbit) on the phone to see if I've recovered enough to push hard in training.

- 5:13 AM Drink coffee, sit with Tracy and the cats for cuddles and play YouTube motivational videos.
- 5:30 AM Perform Wim Hof breathing or State (a mobile app) breathing exercises for ten minutes.
- 5:40 AM Have a two-minute cold shower and change (recently changed to sea dip after coaching TST).
- 5:50 AM Leave for coaching TST online and in-gym.

As you can tell, by the time 6 AM comes, I'm fired up and ready for anything. What could you use to drive up that energy and keep your state high in the morning? What strategy could you employ in your morning routine to see improvements in your confidence? Once you have a consistent, useful morning routine, you'll move from the Change Room to the next room.

3. JOURNEY ROOM

When you're in the Journey Room, you're happy, motivated for change, optimistic and curious. But sometimes you play till you crash, you have too much go-go, and not enough relaxation or noticing what's holding you back. The best strategy for someone stuck in the Journey Room is relaxation therapy of some sort, and more clarity on focus and direction.

Being clearer on intentions and a little more organised in your daily approach works wonders. People in this room are grafters, hustlers and go-getters. But, they sometimes get caught up in the day-to-day grind and miss the opportunities to find more clarity and direction through relaxation or guidance/realignment practice. The great thing is, they're in a pretty good place, but some things still hold them back. Momentum isn't as frequent and fast as they'd like.

Tactics I've found that work amazingly for myself and past and present clients are:

- massage
- meditation
- yoga

- floatation tank
- a detailed next day prep
- morning journaling with constant evaluation of goals/daily intentions (data gathering)
- regular check-ins with a high standard peer group (accountability)

These strategies, once implemented regularly, go a long way. I'm sure that if you find yourself in the Journey Room, you're not paying enough attention to something on this list. You're probably aware of something that could help you blow things up to feel more momentum in your life, allowing you to venture into the next room.

4. LIGHT ROOM

When you're in the Light Room, you have flow and momentum. You're constantly prioritising progress over the forceful need for perfection. You've accepted your flaws and experience mostly calm and self-control. You might be thinking, what the hell does someone regularly need to stay in such a high state? You must think this person has it all figured out. However, the reality is they need a combination of all the tactics mentioned previously.

Someone who feels a nine or ten out of ten has discovered what works *for* them. They've found the most useful routine that leaves them feeling fantastic each day. The structure they apply to their life just works for them, no matter what. The routine may be hard, but they see the value in doing it, so they do it regardless of how they feel. They're committed to seeing progress. They understand they may be tired or feel weak or distracted some days. But this does not stop them. They have a deep trust in the process and know exactly what method makes them feel supercharged in their state and ready for anything.

They use a variety of tactics and come up with their own recipe that works for them. This is where 'one size fits one' instead of 'one size fits all' really comes into play. Most people are looking for the secret to success or that one *hack* that all the millionaires do. Or the one body strategy that will keep them in shape, no matter what. In reality, those who have truly made it work have tried many things before finding what feels good, what works, and what can sustain them long term. That's the hard truth.

> **You build your success and happiness by consistent daily actions of high personal value tasks that create a ripple effect of positive impact in your own life.**

You build your success and happiness by consistent daily actions of high personal value tasks that create a ripple effect of positive impact in your own life.

SUMMARY

The four-room analogy is something I use in my live seminars because of its straight-up power. It quickly identifies where you are emotionally and how you can help navigate your way through to higher states of wellbeing.

The pity party stops here. You have the tools now, and you have the information. Start with where you are and with what you've got. Start making some kind of progress. Use the techniques to manage your state and stop the excuses. If you need further accountability and coaching, seek it out. Don't try and figure it all out on your own.

Remember this about the four rooms. You live in either the Past, Change, Journey or Light Room. You visit other rooms, but you have only one permanent residence. Use the daily action steps advised to move up the rooms and get to a better place mentally.

Bring awareness and attention to where you live in your head. Discover what actions you need to *do* to get yourself to a higher and happier state. Create a plan of action with new daily habits to help your overall emotional wellbeing.

In the next chapter, you'll look at a subject I've struggled with many times over the years, and yet it's also brought me much joy and happiness. Let's talk about relationships.

CHAPTER 8

SUPERCHARGING YOUR RELATIONSHIPS

So far, you've looked at *you* a lot, looking inside at your habits, internal dialogue and challenging your beliefs. This has been helping you discover more about yourself and whether or not what you're currently doing is useful in your life. This chapter shifts the focus onto others. It looks into the relationships you have within your life, how you handle them, what they mean to you and how to best navigate problems.

I will focus mostly on the relationship with those closest to you, and that's your wife, husband, girlfriend, boyfriend, etc. However, I'll talk about other relationships too. Remember, this book is written from a heterosexual male's perspective who's in a long-term relationship with a female. However, regardless of your sexuality or relationship status, you can swing the terms used in this chapter to be relevant to your personal situation.

WHAT IS A HEALTHY RELATIONSHIP?

Simply put, a healthy relationship is one where you're in your best state and on your *best* behaviour. Obviously, there are times when you're tired, angry, hungover, grieving, ill, injured, bored and a whole host of other emotions that change your state temporarily. However, if you're constantly experiencing friction, disagreements, bickerings, arguments and thoughts of how fed up you are, something is clearly not working.

Relationships aren't always designed to make you happy. The purpose of a relationship is to live your highest self. It will *always* test you to do that without fail. Why is it that the ones you love will trigger and test you the most? It's almost like they know which button to press to frustrate the hell out of you.

Only when someone is triggered do they get the opportunity to decide how they respond. Often they lash out, trying to prove themselves right. They may even try to prove the other person wrong using various methods, such as weaponising their insecurities against them, shouting, bawling, swearing and trying to come out of the situation as the 'victor.'

The problem with this egotistical stance within relationships is that there's no real winner or loser. When you think in an "I must win this argument" way, you end up in a perpetual cycle of trying to outdo each other. You use various methods that eventually tear you both down, grind down your confidence and further expose and exaggerate both of your insecurities.

RELATIONSHIPS SUFFER WHEN EGO IS INVOLVED

Ego comes into play in 99% of relationships at some point. As soon as it does, you're faced with the challenge of needing to be right, no matter the cost. However, you shouldn't always think of the ego as bad. It's valuable in your life for certain things. But when it goes unmanaged, gets overinflated, and you feel you have to prove dominance over another, the relationship will struggle to be fulfilling or easy going.

You can guarantee friction and discontent when your ego comes into play too much. In all relationships, there will be disagreements (as there are in my relationship). The problem is exaggerated when you hold unrealistic expectations of your relationships and partners. For example, when you *expect* them to know what you're thinking or, even worse, expect them to make you happy.

Happiness is first and foremost an inside job where you must take responsibility. If you're single right now, and you're relying on someone else to make you happy, you're going to be frequently disappointed. If you're single, when you get into a relationship, you have the opportunity to magnify your happiness and expand together as a team. That doesn't mean you can't grow together if you're already attached to someone (I'll come to that shortly).

I've seen too many people who are miserable because they're single. They feel alone and feel like they're missing out. When I was single, I had a whale of a time. I had loads of time to myself, opportunities to meet new people, go for coffee dates and time to explore new hobbies. I didn't have to think about someone else all the time. I could eat, watch and do more of whatever I wanted. There's a tonne of advantages to being single. Don't think you're miserable and missing out on much if you are. This could be the perfect time for you to do many things you'd love to do, such as finding yourself a little more, trying new hobbies and exploring more.

You can help develop some more independence and create higher personal standards so that you can attract someone who's on your level when they gravitate into your life. It's a great time to develop higher standards when you're single, as you'll put up with less bullshit when you eventually get into a relationship.

I think there's great importance to having some time on your own. My current partner, Tracy, and I have been together for five-plus years as of writing this book, and we're very happy together. But I always say I'm not happy just because I'm with her. We were both previously single and worked on our happiness before getting together. We crossed paths, and, along the way, we've helped expand each other's happiness together. This was because we already had higher standards than in previous relationships. We'd worked on ourselves as individuals before getting involved.

The great thing about having several failed relationships behind you is that there are many lessons you've learnt about yourself, such as where you messed up and where you went wrong. For me, there was a destructive strain of lying, cheating, snorting cocaine at weekends, and being short-tempered with an overinflated ego. Previously, I hated being proved wrong, and I was generally self-centred in my approach. I only thought about what I could get and what a relationship could give me. I never thought about what I could *give* to it.

My past relationships have given me powerful lessons and insights. I can tell you now if you still have the self-centred trait in your personality, don't be surprised when there's conflict and anxiety within your relationship.

MAN AND WOMAN'S GREATEST NEED

When navigating relationships, it's important to be aware of the main masculine (male) and feminine (female) needs in life. The priority and greatest need of the masculine is freedom. He needs to be 'on purpose,' have a professional mission, provide and do his own thing. He needs freedom to act and decide.

The priority and greatest need of the feminine is certainty. The feminine needs to express vulnerability and have security and safety.

As I write this, I need you to be aware both men and women have masculine and feminine energies. At certain times they'll express both sides of these energies. Of course, men will enjoy having certainty and safety, just as many women will love the freedom to be purposeful and have a mission in their professional life, etc.

However, certain people have more masculine or feminine energy. Regardless of where the energy lies, both parties must have the ability to express their highest energy need. For example, let's say there's a woman who has high feminine energy and doesn't get a chance to feel certain enough to love and look after her child. Perhaps she finds herself working too much, taking on too many masculine traits, providing and making strong decisions, etc. In that case, there may be a disconnect within her relationship as she's unable to express her highest energy need often enough.

Another example is the man who is kept away from his mission and work and spends too much time in safety and certainty, not making decisions and taking on challenges. In this case, he'll feel stale and unconfident, and problems could arise in his relationship.

During the Covid lockdowns from 2020 onwards, there was so much talk about the rise of men's mental health problems. Think about how most of these men were stripped of their purpose and ability to be on their mission. Many emotional and relationship problems came about because these men were unable to express their highest energy need.

TWO HALVES OF THE BRAIN

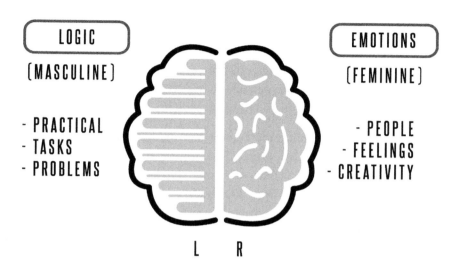

Figure 17: Two Halves Of The Brain Diagram

Did you know scientists have discovered that certain parts of your brain are responsible for different choices? They say the left side of your brain is primarily responsible for logical decision making. This is where productivity, tasks and problem solving come into play. This is the more masculine side of the brain. In contrast, the right side of your brain is primarily responsible for the emotional side of things. This is where your interactions with others, nurturing feelings and creativity lie. You could say this is the more feminine side of the brain (see Figure 17).

You already know that, whether you're male or female, you'll have a variety of left and right brain choices that present themselves every day. The important thing is understanding balance. It's very hard to find a healthy balance within a relationship when one or both parties are stuck on 'one-sided' choices. Let's say your woman has primarily feminine energy yet is expected to solve too many problems, be practical and make too many big decisions during her day, at the expense of expressing her feminine energy? Don't be surprised when there seems to be conflict within your relationship. There needs to be a healthy balance of both, with an understanding of which energy you're both expressing.

Imagine if a man has primarily masculine energy and is taken away from his mission, purpose, and ability to choose freely for too long. Imagine he's wrapped up in too many feelings, comfort, and not having time on his own. Men tend to require solitude periods more than women. He may become withdrawn and feel weak due to not expressing his masculine core energy.

Women with primarily feminine energy (not all, but most women) want a strong man. Please note that strong does not mean rough. They desire and are often attracted to a strong masculine man that knows his purpose and has a mission in life. There's something highly attractive about a man who knows where he's going and is completely certain of himself to a woman.

Likewise, a man with strong masculine energy loves the idea of a nurturing woman who's not just warm and comforting but will perform sexual athletics in bed when required. Deep down, this is the feminine energy that most women crave, but they lack the confidence to express it, mostly because their partner does not appreciate them enough.

LET'S TALK ABOUT SEX

When talking about sex, the last thing you want your intimate life to become is mutual masturbation. Imagine that it's a case of you come, I come, job done! That doesn't deepen your loving connection with another, does it? This is why it's important to understand the need for a good balance of masculine and feminine energy. A man needs time to be on his own, make decisions and strong choices, even lift heavy things, and be 'manly' (for lack of a better word).

Likewise, a woman needs her certainty and reassurance in the form of different acts of love. She needs compliments after trying on a new dress and the ability to be in all the roles she wants with creative freedom, from decorating the home how she sees fit to connecting and interacting with friends as she pleases.

To be more physically strong is a masculine trait. It just so happens that many men have lost their purpose. They've allowed too much comfort and security into their lives, too many takeaways, drinks and TV. Therefore, they've lost their expression of their masculine core, which leads to feeling weaker and less confident. If you're a man reading this and this hits a nerve, maybe it's time to start finding your masculine core again. What could you possibly do this week, or what could you schedule? Who could you speak to, or what could you find out more about that would help express your masculine core? Perhaps you could do a form of martial arts, weightlifting, boxing or other sport? What about archery, axe throwing, riding a motorbike, creating a 'man cave' in the home or shed, or simply spending time with those you trust to talk about 'man' things?

ARE YOU FIXING OR JUSTIFYING?

Justifying instead of fixing is a cause of enormous conflict in relationships. When you're deep in a disagreement, you have to ask yourself if you're trying to fix the problem or are you justifying why you're right or the other is wrong? The ego plays a big role in relationships, so it's important to recognise this. Start to question if your ego is triggered when you come into a disagreement in your relationships.

To combat this, you have to look at both parties. You're probably both guilty of allowing your ego to inflate at times, trying to win or prove an argument or disagreement. Hey, I'm guilty too! These days, however, when things arise, I make a conscious effort to ask myself, "Am I trying to justify myself here, or am I genuinely trying to fix this situation?"

If you are stuck in your ego, you're justifying. If you're fixing, you're being considerate and compassionate. When fixing, you'll find yourself looking for solutions and trying to be useful. Be careful that you're not also trying to get the upper hand. Ultimately, you could be creating a metaphorical point system in your head as to who's won more or done more wrong that you can bring up in a future conversation.

Being a man, I understand this. You want to fix things. It's in your nature. Women want to be heard. Sometimes it's too easy to try and give advice when you should be listening. So here are two great questions that not only help fix the situation if it gets rocky but also allow her to be heard at the same time:

- Is there a way I can make today easier for you?
- Is there anything else that you're not happy with?

Work on being more useful by asking these two questions. Speak in a calmer tone to quickly defuse and reconnect in a disruptive situation. Here's some great advice. If your partner says, "I'm fine," this means you need to dig deeper. When "I'm fine" rears its head, it's covering a deeper issue. Do some more digging compassionately. Try and understand what the deeper problem is and be genuinely curious and helpful. Remember to use the two questions above.

THE FIVE LOVE LANGUAGES

Most relationship issues tend to stem from one or the other feeling unloved. We can all be guilty of thinking we're nice to our partners, but we often don't realise how our miscommunication is causing a disconnect. If your partner is distant or highly reactive, consider for a moment whether they feel loved fully. Are they feeling loved in themselves, and is love being expressed fully by you towards them?

Allow me to introduce you to the five love languages, a concept created by a gentleman named Gary Chapman. He's written several books for singles, those in relationships, kids and teenagers, just to name a few. I can't recommend his work enough, so go ahead and purchase one of his extraordinary books. The following section will simplify and shorten the lessons from his teachings that have transformed my relationships.

As explained before, many problems arise in a relationship due to an overinflated or fragile ego and high expectations unfairly placed over the other person. The five love languages are about how we give and receive love differently. When you fully understand this, these languages can help calm the ego and neutralise expectations on your part. When this happens, both parties feel comforted, connected and loved on a deeper level.

Mr Chapman explains just five ways to give and receive love. You may not realise this if you're only expressing love in the ways that either you're familiar with or you prefer. There's a possibility you're not expressing love in the primary language the other person in your relationship prefers to receive. Therefore, there will always be a disconnect, no matter how nice a person you think you are.

The five love languages are:

1. words

2. acts of service

3. gifts

4. quality time

5. physical touch

Let's break each one down so that not only can you discover your love language, you can identify your partner's language. Also, it's not just for intimate relationships. You could use these findings to identify the preferred love language for your parents, close friends, and even your kids or coworkers.

1. WORDS

These are spoken or written words of affirmation or appreciation. Everyone loves to hear nice things about them. No one actively thrives by hearing negative or hurtful comments. Consider if you feel the most loved when you hear nice things said in one way or another. It could be a compliment about how you look or perform on a certain task. Or it could be an "I love you" text or a voice note from your partner that says, "Just want you to know how sexy you look and how much I still fancy you." Would you personally feel most loved when receiving words?

Of course, you'd probably like hearing or reading things like this, and you'd be appreciative of it at any time. But is this your primary way of feeling loved, i.e., your most appreciated way? Would your partner feel most loved when you express this language to them?

2. ACTS OF SERVICE

Acts of service could be doing your washing, ironing your clothes, or making sure that dinner is on the table after a hard day at work. It could be taking the kids to school, sorting out the bank trip, or booking and organising the holiday. They're the little acts of service that make your life easier and less stressful. Maybe you were brought up where your mother did everything for you, and you appreciate that now as an adult? Do you feel most appreciated and loved when your partner does these acts of service?

Everyone appreciates these acts of service, but is it your primary love language? Would you prefer it to the first love language, which was words? What about your partner? If you're a man and work long and hard hours and love it when your clothes are in the drawer neatly folded each day or food is ready on the table, consider that your primary love language may be acts of service.

Imagine your partner tells you lovely things all day about how wonderful you are, but they don't do these acts you appreciate. You're sure to feel some sort of disconnect, even though your partner is doing their best. If your *primary* language isn't fulfilled, you're not going to feel fully and deeply loved. It works exactly the same way with your partner too.

3. GIFTS

Gifts, as a love language, usually mean receiving something physical. It can be bought or made, and it's presented as a gift, wrapped or unwrapped. Maybe you feel most excited and deeply loved when you're given a gift? It doesn't necessarily mean you're materialistic (it's ok if you are, by the way).

It could be a new handbag, a holiday, a house or a car. It could be flowers, a video game, a magazine, aftershave or perfume, food, books, something for the house or something that makes things easier at work. It could be expensive, cheap or even free. If gifts are your primary love language, imagine if you never get anything physical to hold in your hands or maybe proudly display. Even if you hear regular loving words and your partner does regular acts of service, there will be a disconnect if you're without the gifts you'd like.

As you can see, there are many ways to feel appreciated. Perhaps you're starting to discover your partner's love language or your own primary love language. If the three languages so far don't strike you as important in the grand scheme of it all, perhaps what you crave most is the next love language.

4. QUALITY TIME

Are you always asking, "When can we have time, just the two of us?" Or perhaps you find yourself complaining about how much time your partner spends on their phone or how much time they put in at work? These are clues. If you're always asking or complaining about time, your primary love language is likely to be quality time.

This is where a lot of disconnect lies within relationships. For example, the man works all day and comes home tired. He just wants to eat, watch an hour of TV and go to bed. Even if that man provides for his partner and gives them the house, car, technology and fancy stuff, no amount of it will connect like quality time if that's their partner's primary language. If their partner feels they get no time together, they're left feeling underappreciated.

This is where date nights are critical to so many relationships as an expression of quality time. Notice it's not the *quantity* of time. It's quality of time. This means a date does not have to be massively long. Even an hour or two where you leave your phone at home, look into her eyes and deeply connect, and ask her questions about her day, week, and life will do. Give her your biggest gift, which is your presence, your undivided attention and quality time. I see this disconnect in many relationships where one person is going without the focused attention and presence of the other. This can be through too much time spent at work or on technology. It lessens the quality of attention.

5. PHYSICAL TOUCH

All physical affection and intimacy come into play here, not just sex, although that's a big part. After all, there's no deeper and more intimate connection than intercourse with the one you love. But what goes unchecked often is the hugging, kissing, holding hands on a walk, stroke of the back while washing dishes, a casual smack of the arse as your partner walks up the stairs, kissing their neck in bed or snuggling before sleep.

Regular physical touch signifies a healthy, long-lasting and exciting relationship. Unless one person is celibate, every touch, kiss, squeeze or sexual act brings a closer connection within the relationship. If you're going weeks or even months without sex, you're likely to be experiencing a lack of physical touch and affection. Also, it's hard to switch from 'no touch' to deep, manic sex. You may find yourself needing to get drunk or going for mutual masturbation or mechanical sex when you neglect physical touch. That's not a deeply intimate and connecting relationship, is it?

On the whole, most of us are physical people who appreciate another person's touch. However, you may think that physical touch is not your *primary* love language. Perhaps you're not a touchy-feely kind of person? Be warned, if touch is unexpressed for long periods, your relationship will stagnate, whether you like it or not. This is especially true if your or your partner's love language is physical touch. Don't settle for a weekly peck on the cheek or be someone who has to be asked to hug their kids.

USING THE LOVE LANGUAGES

By now, you should have discovered your love language and perhaps even identified your partner's language or that of someone else who's close to you. Perhaps you've identified that you have more than one love language? That's ok as you'll likely have a primary language which is the one you use most often. Which language comes up most frequently for you?

If you've identified your close partner's language, perhaps you've understood that you're not expressing love towards them in ways you now know you should. Is this why you're currently experiencing friction within your relationship? This could be the start of something new for you both.

If you're feeling a little less connected than you'd like, and you're now aware of your partner's language, it's important you start expressing that specific language frequently. Don't use your love language or express love the way you're used to giving. Start expressing *their* preferred primary love language and see if the relationship starts to flow and become more intimate with less friction.

Here's a key point. Don't expect your partner to reciprocate straight away. Start with what you now know, with where you are. Be as consistent as you can for the next two to three weeks and give without expectation of return. You'll start noticing a change if you correctly identify your partner's language and express it frequently enough. Are they not giving you fulfilment in your preferred love language? Consider bringing up this section of the book to them and talking about it together openly. Or, of course, you could buy one of Gary Chapman's books. I can't recommend them highly enough.

SUMMARY

It's important in any relationship to lead by example, to take responsibility for your half, how you act and how you respond. Don't wait for the other person to live up to your expectations. Take an honest self-assessment of how you're behaving. Are you expressing love in their language? Don't just think of yourself.

Once you've applied your partner's particular love language enough times, there will be a point in time when you can discuss how they could reciprocate using your love language in a way that's most fulfilling to you. It's important to start with the current knowledge about where you are right now. It could just take a few extra nice words or a handwritten note. Perhaps leave that project at work till tomorrow so you can bathe the kids or have dinner with your partner and not leave them alone for another night. The simple things matter. Don't deny the simplicity in these acts. Remember, your partner cares what you *do*, not what you say you're going to do or should have done.

These techniques solve a lot of relationship problems. Please use them. If you find yourself using these languages and techniques for a prolonged period and the relationship isn't what you believed it was or could be, what is the worst-case scenario? It's never wasted time, as all relationships are valuable lessons. It just highlights you're in the wrong relationship, and that's ok. You'll not stay a victim over what was or what could or should have been. You'll see it as it is, not worse than it is. Moving forward, you'll choose personal empowerment over victimhood.

The final chapter moves into the world of work, where we all spend most of our lives. Maybe you hate your job, would love to start a business, or see some growth in yourself professionally. Here's where I discuss how to be happier and more productive in your job or business. I'm going to discuss all my eye-opening insights from the past nine-plus years of being self-employed, transitioning from a full-time employed plumber to a self-employed life coach, and everything in between. Strap yourself in for the ride!

CHAPTER 9

SUPERCHARGING
YOUR WORLD OF WORK

A little over nine years ago, I was a full-time plumber for a local firm up in the north east of England. I started as an apprentice serving four years until I was fully qualified and served a further four years as a competent trade professional. I replaced old toilets, bathroom suites and heating systems with new ones in domestic properties.

Admittedly, in my first four to five years, I was having fun, enjoying a new skill and trade, and feeling secure in my full-time position. At one point, there was an opportunity to progress into management. I took the test and attended the interviews, but I didn't get the promotion. In hindsight, I wasn't the right guy for the job. At times, I had a negative attitude, was not always reliable, and was too young to appreciate the workload. Plus, I complained a lot, just like most people I worked alongside.

I met some great people, such as my old mentors, Stevie D and Gary U, who went to work in Iraq during the war. I made friends like Matty F, who attempted the world record of stuffing 40 grapes in his mouth without chewing. I still appreciate these lads to this day. But, somewhere along the way, I felt I was outgrowing my life. Even though I had a secure job, holiday pay, sick pay, an Audi car on finance, and a mortgage, I felt stuck. I was miserable day-to-day in the latter years. I was unfulfilled and unchallenged. I compensated by snorting cocaine at weekends, indulging in other drugs and substances, and having a string of broken relationships. It was a downward spiral of negative choices.

I decided to take my personal training qualification at weekends and move to a new profession. I then got a business mentor, Chris Brown, a top guy who helped me get started and fill spaces for my outdoor boot camp. This progressed to a function room upstairs from a bar and then onto my own private gym unit, which I still own to this day.

There were a lot of ups and downs along the way, of course, but I wanted to give you a brief background to explain how I've gone from full-time employment to self-employed entrepreneur. Regardless of where you are in your life professionally, even if you're not currently working, this next section will help you assess and evaluate your position and help you either change completely or upgrade your current experience.

The world of work is part of your mission and purpose. Your professional position is there not only to provide for you and others but to give you purpose, structure and priority in your life. It gives you something to *do*. As a result, you earn a wage, feel significant to others and feel something positive in return for your efforts.

Your work is likely to take up the majority of your time. You spend a lot of your week working, so feeling somewhat happy with your position makes sense. After all, you choose to be where you are. Don't be naive and think you don't have a choice and *have* to be where you are right now. You don't. You're completely free to choose a new career, job, venture, etc., whenever you please. The obvious thing stopping you is the fear of letting go and adopting uncertain change, and that's completely understandable.

MENTAL FEARS THAT CRIPPLE OUR WORLD OF WORK

ANXIETY OVER MONEY

This has been a huge one for me and not just since I stepped out of full-time employment. It's in-built into 99% of society, and it's completely understandable and acceptable. Most people find it difficult to let go of the constant worrying over money from a young age. You're not alone in this fear of "what if" or "what when." I still have these thoughts from time to time, even though I do pretty well for myself.

I'll briefly discuss better management and understanding of money as I move on to help you gain more self-control over those disempowering thoughts. Just to be clear, even millionaires and high-end businessmen still have anxiety over money. I've met many of them, and they all say, "More money doesn't always mean fewer problems." In fact, it can cause *more* problems and more stress because you could lose more money or even *waste* more money.

BEING REJECTED

Whether you're self-employed or employed full-time, the fear of rejection frequently stops you from progressing in many ways. Whether it's someone saying no to your product or service or getting the "unsuccessful at this time" response for that job interview you prepared so hard for, feeling rejected is crippling to your appreciation of your work.

When you feel rejected, you're likely to stop taking further risks and therefore feel stuck in your current position. I'll talk about strategy and mindset in the coming pages, but remember that rejection is a choice. You can only feel rejected if you choose to. No one is choosing your feelings but you. That's a hard pill to swallow, but it'll save you a lot of heartache and frustration.

FEELING INCOMPETENT

There's nothing more embarrassing and degrading than feeling you're not cut out for the job, that you can't handle the pressure, or that you're taking on more than you can handle. This is a legitimate fear for many people. However, you can handle it by raising your self-confidence.

Use the techniques discussed earlier in the book, such as the seven daily habits from Chapter 2, to become more organised and a better communicator of your message. I believe everyone is much more competent than they think they are. They just allow their own and others' opinions to hold them back. This leads me to the next topic.

'COMPARISONITIS'

This is the fear of where you think you should be compared to where you are. It's constantly gauging your perceived results against someone else's results rather than looking at your *actual* results. It's when you live a fantasy in your mind over the reality of where you are. These are all examples of picking drama over actual data.

Looking at someone else's success on social media or within your organisation or peer group and thinking you *should* be further ahead is a surefire way to dishearten you. It will lead you to a more anxiety-filled, overwhelmingly pressured situation. When you choose not to accept what is and project what should be, you'll feel frustrated because you're not where you say you want to be.

There are ways around this, such as using the 'data over drama' strategy I revealed in Chapter 3 to raise self-confidence and your general state.

THE MANAGER AND THE LEADER

You've seen the pictures of the manager barking orders *at* the workforce and the leader at the front, supposedly depicting the major differences. However, before letting that influence you, think of yourself as a leader *and* a manager.

A manager tends to do things right. A leader tends to do the right things. You need to be both in your professional life, no matter what you do or where you are. You need to manage your time but lead from the front with actions that help yourself and others. Manage in a way that keeps others on track and on time, but lead in a way that others aspire to follow. Problems will happen when you're always waiting for instructions, asking for permission and not taking any initiative. Or even worse, you're not attempting to go the extra mile because you think you're stuck in your current position and may be frustrated that you don't get paid enough.

While I hear you and understand you may feel underpaid and overworked at times, the reality is you get paid based on the value you bring to the marketplace. Whether employed or self-employed, the mindset of "I've always been this way" or "we've always done it this way" is a quick route to stagnation and enormous problems. This is especially the case in this ever-changing world where people's expectations and communication, interaction, and even pay are always evolving. You, too, must roll with the times and be open to taking on new roles and techniques, not complaining so much but leading from the front while also managing the way you do things along the journey.

OVERWHELM OR OVERLOAD

Quite simply, overwhelm or overload is the lack of clarity on your priorities. Put it this way. When you're fully engaged and know what needs to be done, when you have a clear, concise, focused plan, and you're fully immersed in the work, do you get frustrated and think of how overwhelmed you're feeling? Probably not. You become overwhelmed only when you allow your thoughts of "too much to do, too little time" to get in the way. This is easily done.

Of course, most of the world may expect you to be in five places at once with three sets of hands and eyes in the back of your head. However, when you're in a state of flow and clear on what is a priority for you (you can't make everything a priority), you often forget how much you feel you have to do and glide through tasks with ease. Let's delve into dealing with these issues over the next few pages.

TAKING YOUR PROFESSIONAL LIFE TO THE NEXT LEVEL

Throughout this book, you've been given several techniques to impact several areas of your life. You can apply most of those techniques to your professional life, whether in a workplace environment, building or improving a business, or even with your studies. Several lifestyle habits are very valuable to you. For example, you can switch health around to apply to business or work. The simplicity in certain things often goes overlooked when you're too stuck in one way of operating.

RESPONSIBILITY

Whether you're a student, employee, manager or business owner, the same principles apply. They just need to be moulded to your particular position to fit with where you currently are in your professional life. You're entirely responsible for how far you can progress professionally. If you feel you're stuck in a dead-end job and believe there's no room for progression, and yet you choose to stay there, you're actively keeping yourself stuck. There are jobs out there, several thousand jobs, and there are plenty of business opportunities too. Right now, we're living in an age where you can start selling things from your garage or bedroom, on eBay or Facebook Marketplace, and become profitable within a few days.

Remember, you're paid based on the *value* you bring to the marketplace. If you're in a job and you're sick of feeling undervalued, consider first whether or not you bring a lot of value to that company. A hard question to answer is, are you replaceable? I know it's a difficult question, but could someone else come along tomorrow, take your job, and do what you do to the level you do it, no questions asked? If the answer is yes, you need to figure out ways to become more valuable to the company or person who employs you so they can't afford to let you go. Do you go the extra mile without complaining? Are you reliable and trustworthy enough to always get the job done on time? Are you friendly and approachable, or reactive and filled with pessimism and low energy?

This is often a harsh wake-up call when it comes to honest self-assessment. Some people are just doing the bare minimum to get paid and expecting too much from those higher up. They're expecting things to just fall into their laps. It simply doesn't work that way.

I've been self-employed for nine years with a six-figure business. If you're in a business like me, and if all the sales rely on you, you have to ask yourself, "Am I valuable to the marketplace? Am I truly giving enough value that others can see, and am I an expert in my field? Am I putting across enough value that people would want to invest time, energy and money?"

You may have to go and study some more. You may have to change your methods completely and have awkward conversations with clients and people around you. Sometimes you have to invest in new mentors and coaches to help push you to grow and stay accountable to new ways of getting things done. You have to start being seriously open-minded and optimistic when it comes to new business, making sales and getting things organised to be a profitable and powerful business or enterprise. The days of "it's always been this way" are over.

Here's some great advice for better organisation and less stress regarding money.

MANAGE WHAT YOU ALREADY HAVE

Debt is one of those things that I understand is necessary at times. But if you want to be a professional, getting into crazy debt for a holiday, house or car is just madness. Yes, a mortgage is valuable to many people, as is a car. But do you really need that £20,000 loan for a new conservatory? Is buying the latest BMW and adding a further £60,000 debt to your name necessary? Do you need the six-bedroom house on the newest estate when only three people would live there? Is the £8,000 cosmetic surgery a must-have right now?

You will always find the money for what you value the highest, no matter what. You'll beg, steal, borrow, work overtime and do what it takes if you value it highly enough. Remember that. To actively get into debt for something you don't *need* and just *want* because you are too impatient or just need to show it off to try and prove a point is just plain stupid.

If you have the money and it won't put you in debt, great. If not, think about the power in *delayed* gratification. That is, waiting for things. Yes, you need a home and a car, but probably not all the other stuff. In my early 20s, I got a £9,000 loan for an Audi, which I didn't need in hindsight. It just looked good and was a nice drive. Over time, it cost me an additional £9,000 in repairs. I finally sold it for £900, a tenth of the purchase cost. £18,000 turned into £900 and a load of time in the garage. What a great example of an unworthy investment! I now lease a non-flashy Nissan to get around hassle-free.

Your money and time are your most precious commodities. Managing these assets is critical to your financial and professional success and your emotional stability in your professional life. There's nothing worse than worrying about money and living paycheck to paycheck, having "too much month left at the end of the money." There is a way to tackle this. Read on.

WRITE DOWN EVERYTHING THAT YOU SPEND

Are you taking inventory of what you spend? You'll likely know what money comes in throughout the month. But do you write down everything that you spend? I have this little notebook that cost 40p at Wilkos (household goods store). Every day, I write down everything that I bought. I track every outgoing.

Write your purchases down if you want to get your finances in order. Every can of fizzy drink or juice, newspaper, lunch, Amazon purchase, upgrade on the car, alcoholic drink, or any outgoing, write it down. With clarity on what you've spent at the start or end of each month, you can ascertain where your money is going. This is using data over drama. Track what's been spent on household bills, entertainment, food, alcohol, Netflix and online subscriptions, gambling, shopping, education, etc. Then, segment them into categories. The categories I use are:

- business
- household bills
- food (shopping)
- food (eating out or convenience buys)
- regular outgoings (bills, etc.)
- subscriptions
- one-off purchases

I attempt to reduce the outgoing expenditure each month. I make sure I do this on the first of each month, reflecting on the previous. I total up each month, review and then decide what is unnecessary and needs to go. Every-thing, when written clearly, helps you gain complete clarity on managing what you have. This lightens the load of your emotions behind managing your money.

SAVE AS SOON AS YOU GET PAID

Either at the start of each month or on your payday, put 10% of your earnings away to one side. You can opt for a savings account you won't touch. Even better, put that money into some kind of investment, such as a Moneybox account (an investment app), a recommended online trading platform, or some other results-backed investment opportunity where your money can grow and work *for* you.

It's eye-opening to see how much your money goes up once you immediately get rid of 10% of your earnings. The term is 'pay yourself first.' After all, you deserve to be compensated for your efforts in this life.

Some people pay everyone and everything else before themselves. That's a really bad habit. It doesn't fill your mind with certainty, and you'll always doubt yourself when making decisions linked to your finances. Every time you pay yourself first, you make sure you're becoming more disciplined about putting money aside. At the same time, you're increasing your self-worth by paying and investing in yourself.

You'll not miss that 10%. You may think you'll need it, but the more a habit it becomes, the more you don't miss that 10%. You'll be surprised at just how quickly that pot builds when you start adopting this strategy. Make it a rule and your minimum standard for a stronger financial and professional position.

I recommend you read The Richest Man in Babylon by George S. Classon to get a deeper understanding.

LOOKING AFTER YOUR EXISTING CUSTOMERS

If you're currently in a job or own a business, you'll have existing customers. People who already know, like and trust you (or the company you work for). Keeping them happy is crucial to maintaining a strong, profitable business and lifestyle.

Retaining customers is always easier than constantly getting new ones. It's surprising how obsessed people become with attracting new clients or finding new customers when there's a whole bunch of people they're not paying much attention to who trust them enough to spend money again and again with them.

Around 20% of your existing customer base is ready to buy more from you and more often. But only if you treat them right and ask for the sale. Imagine if you're in a job and get 20% of the existing clients or customers to double their monthly spend with your company. Then imagine they go on to sing your praises for introducing them to the upgraded product or service because they're experiencing better results. How do you think your boss would view you if you successfully increased those customers' spending? Do you think it'd improve your chances of promotion? Damn right it would!

Likewise, if you're self-employed, imagine if 20% of your customers repeated their purchase of your product or service for the next six months. All because you treated them a little better and asked them about their needs moving forward. Remember, people buy from people. And you, my friend, are a damn good person deep down, I'm sure of it. I imagine you've solved some pretty big problems in some way in your professional life. How could you possibly solve those problems even more quickly for your existing customers? Or solve them over a longer period, so the customer is free from these problems long-term?

Clients, customers, and even businesses are people who love to be recognised. Look them in the eyes, give them a firm handshake when meeting them (don't go overboard and break their hand), smile at them, be sure to use their name when speaking to them, and make them feel heard and listened to. Ask them questions that get them thinking about their future with and without you and your product or service. Regularly remind them of the value they get and how it benefits their own life and the lives of others around them.

These simple tidbits of advice often get ignored but have a massive impact on the know, like and trust factor of the human expressing them. That human is *you,* my friend. Your body language and tone of voice could literally make you rich and help you have a more ongoing successful and fulfilling professional life. Don't overlook this advice.

GENERATING NEW BUSINESS

When it comes to attracting new business, there's a tonne of business-related books you could read about generating more leads, making sales, converting more higher paying customers into lifetime revenue, etc. But I want you to consider the mindset of selling and generating new business leads in the following paragraphs.

When it comes to people parting with their money, especially with someone they don't know or a company they've never heard of, there's always going to be resistance and hesitance. An overlooked fact is that people buy when they're *ready* to buy. Sometimes this is forgotten, so people get angry and upset when they ask once or twice and get rejected. These people often let that rejection turn into a fear of asking someone else for a new sale.

Did you know that 80% of sales are done around the 12th contact or beyond? That sounds crazy, right? You put an advert on Facebook. Someone enquires, "How much?" You tell them, and they ghost you. Have you experienced this before? I know it all too well. But the '12 points of contact' idea is interesting. For example, it could take five emails, a Facebook post, an advert, a text, two phone calls and three videos before someone decides to part with their cash and give you new business.

This is relevant in all sales, no matter what you do. People need to trust you before they give you money. Yes, there's a tonne of great questions you could ask and sales training you could implement when trying to persuade. However, having been self-employed for nine years, I can honestly say selling is so much easier when you don't force it. Always ask for the sale, but give value first. Send emails and voice notes, check in with someone, and create valuable text posts or videos on social media that people can digest at their leisure. I'd also recommend having some form of paid advertisement that regularly runs so that you're always top of mind when your customer is ready to buy. This is regardless of what product or service you're offering.

If you're in a job, all of the above remains relevant. What value could you bring to the marketplace that potential customers could recognise? What could you show them that would help them invest in you on behalf of the company? Which, in turn, could allow you to make the sale and guide them through the process of whatever it is you do.

Even successfully selling broadband over the phone can be about building a connection with someone. You could learn their name, what shows they like to watch, 'banter' (amusing, joking talk) about what new films are coming out at the cinema, etc. Conversations on shared interests build a great connection from the get-go. Asking great high-quality questions linked to their desires and main pain points is also foundational when a prospect is looking for someone to trust. Someone that could truly help them with what they want. Where could you be having more conversations like this with potential customers?

Years ago, I made a daily video series on Facebook called 'The #Dailyboom.' I'd done over a thousand episodes live, back-to-back, sharing stories from my life. I talked about films I'd watched, things I'd experienced and the current studies I was doing. I shared the lessons learned and brought daily inspiration and passion to people's lives. I firmly believe to this day that it was the consistent value (I created 1,000 plus videos in a row) that compelled people to watch regularly and made me a trusted authority in the world of expanding people's lives and energy levels. It's partly why I have an ongoing successful and profitable business to this day.

What could you do to give consistent value to your potential clients and customers daily? What could you *give* to feel a sense of contribution and share value with the marketplace?

Get this nailed down, be relentlessly consistent and do not stop. Eventually, on top of applying time-tested business skills such as building relationships, making an irresistible offer and being certain that you can solve the customer or client's specific problem, you'll reap the rewards of your efforts.

You can't force this process. It takes a while and a lot of leg work. You must be willing to sacrifice your comfort and be willing to accept rejection many times over. Use failures as lessons and setbacks as stepping stones for serious comebacks. Remind yourself who benefits when you stay the course. Your family needs this. *You* need this, my friend. What will help you the most is remembering those out there who need you. You're far more needed than you think you are.

TWO STEPS TO DESTROYING OVERWHELM OR OVERLOAD

No matter who you are in your professional life, you'll experience these two feelings at some point. It's only natural when you're in a position of taking on more challenges and desiring to grow. You'll also be faced with many people who want your attention. You'll wish you had another pair of hands and could be in three places at once. I know all about this. I talked about it a lot in my first book, How To Stop Overthinking, which received high praise on Amazon.

When it comes to feeling overwhelmed or overloaded, you only have two choices, or you'll crumble. Let's look at those two choices.

1. CREATE SPACE

There are two parts to this which are remove and delegate.

    a. **Remove anything (or anyone) that's non-essential to your progress or current mission.**

This could be visible distractions, such as too much stuff on your work desk cluttering up your main space sapping your focus and creativity. It could be that the vehicle you drive to other locations requires a deep clean. It could be your phone distracting you and tempting you to scroll on social media.

Think about turning off certain notifications on your devices that aren't useful to you. Think about deleting apps that distract you or you don't use often. Clear out your email inbox and hit mass delete at the start of the month to eliminate all the junk. If it's truly important, send it to another folder. Purchase a kitchen safe to lock away anything that distracts you for a certain period of focused time. Get rid of anything just lying around in your office space, home space or car space that's not useful to you. Clearing your visual space gives you a clearer mental capacity for making better decisions and reducing overwhelm.

Another point on creating space is removing things from your life, such as people and projects. Say no more often if it doesn't fit where you say you want to go. Clearing space in your diary will give you space for a health plan, gym time, a sauna, massage or something of therapeutic value that will help you feel more relaxed. Make space for yourself as well as your to-do list. Don't prioritise your schedule. Instead, schedule your priorities. Health and family should be on that list of priorities.

b. Delegate anything that can be done by someone else.

Get a cleaner for your home. Find someone who can send texts and emails on your behalf. Hire a virtual assistant or in-house person to do the things outside of your skillset, or just odds and ends that someone would happily do for a minimum wage. Could a family member or some-one you know come and clean your house once a week, blitz the garden, or cook your meals? You'll free up more of your own valuable time to do higher-value tasks.

When you learn the art of delegating the smaller tasks, you can free up more energy to tackle the bigger tasks. Those tasks bring more return on investment so that you can keep other people in their jobs. You'll feel more fulfilled when you value your time more. You'll give the absolute best of yourself with the highest energy you can because you're not distracted doing the work that takes away your powerful energy. You get to keep your energy for more important, higher-value tasks that have a greater impact.

2. INCREASE CAPACITY

There are two parts to this which are improve and upgrade.

a. Improve your physical body.

There are several things you know you can probably improve upon. But there is one thing that is a surefire way to keep you progressing professionally, and that's improving your physical body. I know I've already discussed the impact of great physical health on your energy and confidence. However, thinking about its impact on your world of work could take you to the next level professionally.

I remember hearing a true story about a rich businessman, let's call him Martin, who got fat and out of shape from working too hard. His friends used to joke to him that he couldn't see his dick anymore. He wasn't bothered by their comments. His kids poked fun at his big belly. His best friend's wife told him, "Martin, your wife doesn't find you attractive anymore, and she doesn't really want to sleep with you." His sister said, "Martin, you'll not live to see your grandkids grow up if you continue like this." None of this bothered him. Until someone said, "Martin, you being fat is costing you money." Martin responded intensely with, "What?! What do you mean? How?" He wanted to know more.

After further assessment of his attitudes in business, Martin made several discoveries. Even though he was already making good money, he was losing over $1,000,000 in revenue per calendar year because of his low self-confidence, energy levels, falling asleep in meetings, etc. Do you think Martin got in shape after hearing this? Damn right he did.

Regardless of your stance on Martin valuing money more highly than the other things in his life, the point is that everyone has their specific motivations for getting healthy. Of course, most of us will agree that we should all live healthy for our kids, grandkids, partner, etc., and our general health, so we don't have a heart attack or other serious health issues. But think of the lesson behind this story from a professional standpoint.

Without a doubt, being fat and out of shape is costing you money in some capacity. You could be making fewer sales because you're too tired, forgetting to follow up on deals, or falling asleep in meetings. Perhaps you're choosing easier options because of your self-confidence. Maybe some people choose not to do business with you because of how you treat your body.

Like it or not, people judge people. If, for example, a successful investor comes to you who looks after himself and feels, after looking at you, that you aren't disciplined with your body, he may think you're not disciplined in other areas and decide to go elsewhere. This is a possibility and just one of the many reasons you should start improving your physical health. Improve your diet and body to positively impact your professional career as well as the rest of your life. Imagine having more energy for studying and for selling and serving. Imagine having a more pleasant, less stressful workday when you're feeling more healthy, full of energy and enthusiastic about your life.

In doing so, you'll increase your physical and mental capacity to make sales, handle rejections and better deal with all the professional problems you face day-to-day. You'll increase your capacity for focused attention and study time, not to mention being a more positive influencer and showing people you care more for the finer details.

b. Upgrade your skills

What practical skills do you need to upgrade? What mindset issues do you need to upgrade? What organisational skills need looking at within yourself or your company? Is there more planning you could do? Perhaps you could delegate more skills to other people so you can upgrade what matters most to you?

There are always places you can upgrade personally. Somewhere, there's always an opportunity to do so. You should be learning something completely new to you at least once or twice a year. You probably know what you're not very good at already, so it's easy to just stick with what you know, right? If there's no upgrading on your behalf, there's no growth. Without growth, there's no progress. Without progress, there is no happiness. Ultimately your business or professional life will crumble and fall.

Where can you plan an upgrade this coming week? Who do you need to speak to? Which course should you book? Which group do you need to join? Where in your life do you feel you need to upgrade the most professionally to experience more capacity in dealing with overwhelm and overload?

SUMMARY

Organisation is key. You can mix and intertwine organisational skills both personally and professionally to help you keep moving forward with less stress and more flow. A more organised professional life leads to a more organised personal life. Increasing capacity through clearing physical space, improving and upgrading physical health, and organisational efforts will give you more professional space to help everyone involved.

By adopting these philosophies into your professional life, you'll communicate better with customers and clients and build a more effective network by treating yourself better. You'll treat others better too, as you're less likely to be stressed or have a snappy attitude. You'll no longer be going through the motions but *growing* through the motions.

CLOSING THOUGHTS

I wrote this book to be a tidal wave of positive impact. This means it shouldn't just hit you, but all those close to you too. A true leader inspires others to lead, not just to follow. I want you to understand the core principles and philosophies within this book and take with you what works *for* you. Given the usual percentages, the likelihood is that you'll only actively use around 20% or less of this book unless you implement further accountability and a structured routine for executing my advice. But make what you do use count.

Remember, consistency over intensity. Your discipline is not to be applied just when you feel like it. Operate based upon what you're committed to and what you said you'd do, not what you feel like in the moment. If you want to be physically healthy, use the seven daily habits in Chapter 2. Maximise your life to an eight, nine and ten out of ten by applying those simple habits daily. Do them all and stay dedicated. Remember, once they become habits, you won't need motivation.

Which habit is the most important one? The most important one is the *next* one. It's the next meal, the next sleep, the next workout, the next drink, or the next morning. Stop judging your early efforts when you feel rubbish at something. Upgrade your peer group. Pay attention to what you watch, listen and read. Feed your mind with more positive actions and influences. You get what you focus on.

Be as clear and precise as you can about how you want to feel and what you want to experience more and less of in your life. Review your progress daily, weekly and monthly. Be grateful in advance. Set a daily activity that gets you excited. Top up your heart with self-care. Balance your brain with data over drama. Be nice to others, especially if they've ever helped or supported you. Be valuable by protecting your energy and confidence. Motivation doesn't last, but discipline always does. 'Losing your shit' benefits no one. Instead, get M.A.D (Must Act Determined). If you're still intimate with your partner, something is working. Get to bed one hour earlier.

Act your way out of problems. Make a salad sexy. Breathe deep. Make your chest tall and your focus present. Wherever there is optimism, there is opportunity. Don't let pessimism pummel your progress. If something doesn't work, don't be quick to label it broken. Your confidence has no limit. Lead by example, not by opinion. Movement is medicine. Health is wealth. You are enough.

Keep this mantra in mind:

- Make clear the vision.
- Commit to the long game.
- Trust in the process.
- Get excited for the day.

RESOURCES

Throughout this book, I've given you details of resources that help you implement the ideas I've outlined quickly and precisely.

Here's a list of them all for your convenience.

1. The Seven Daily Habits Personal Checklist:

2. Big-Ass Salad Ideas (video):

3. Become a client of mine within the TST. Train your body and your mindset with me online on Zoom:

4. I recommend you find yourself a fantastic sports massage therapist. Check out Mr Graeme Ford on Instagram at @fordyjarra to get insights on sports massage.

5. I recommend watching Relentless, featuring the former professional wrestler, DDP (Diamond Dallas Page), available on Amazon Prime.

6. I recommend State (currently available only on Apple) as a smart guided breathing app.

7. I recommend Moneybox app as a simple way to save and invest. It can round up your purchases to the nearest pound and set aside the spare change. Available on both Apple and Android.

ENDNOTES

1. https://www.momsteam.com/dehydration/water-enhances-sports-performance

2. https://www.theguardian.com/environment/2021/mar/25/uk-flying-blind-on-levels-of-toxic-chemicals-in-tap-water

3. https://www.biri.org/pdf/books/Your-Bodys-Many-Cries-for-Water.pdf

4. https://www.youtube.com/watch?v=Oq28WJpZfLg

5. https://www.youtube.com/watch?v=9Ffceu672c4

6. https://www.forbes.com/sites/nicolefisher/2019/03/06/americans-sit-more-than-anytime-in-history-and-its-literally-killing-us/?sh=7fe79450779d

7. https://www.youtube.com/watch?v=tybOi4hjZFQ

BIBLIOGRAPHY

Harrison, Luke. *How to Stop Overthinking*, UK: Let's Tell Your Story Publishing, 2017.

John, Dan. *Intervention*, USA: On Target Publications, 2013.

John, Dan. *Can You Go?*, *USA:* On Target Publications, 2015.

John, Dan. *Never Let Go, USA:* On Target Publications, 2019.

Chapman, Gary. *The 5 Love Languages: The Secret to Love that Lasts*, USA: Moody Publishers, 2015.

Chapman, Gary. *The 5 Love Languages Singles Edition: The Secret That Will Revolutionize Your Relationships*, USA: Moody Publishers, 2017.

Classon, George S. *The Richest Man in Babylon*, USA: Penguin Books, 1926.

KEEP IN TOUCH

I'd love to hear from you directly about how this book has impacted you, what kinds of results you've had from applying these principles, and the general successes you've experienced so far in your life. I'd also love to hear from you if you have any further questions. I'm here to give the best service I possibly can to help you move forward. You can email me directly at:

Luke@superchargedbooks.com

You can also find me on social media:

Instagram: @lukejohnharrison

Facebook: Luke John Harrison

YouTube: Luke John Harrison

Do you want faster results?

If you want to get results faster and go further with a coach who can hold you accountable, push you and challenge you to do what you said you would do, you could work with me directly. I may be able to help you with either a tailored one-to-one package, a new challenge, within my Total Supercharged Tribe, or perhaps through my higher-end 'Empire' program.

Whatever you need help with, email me directly at:

Luke@superchargedbooks.com

I appreciate you.

Luke